ANTIDOTE

MY COMMITMENT TO THRIVE WITH KIDNEY DISEASE

HIRAL PATEL

E-book ISBN: 978-1-7361685-0-9

ISBN: 978-1-7361685-1-6

CONTENTS

DEDICATION

*To the young boy and his family who gave me an extended journey in Life.
I am forever grateful and hope that I have made you proud.*

*To everyone who has lived with or supported someone through kidney
disease: We are all in this together, and together we will thrive.*

*To Manu and Jyotika Patel,
my parents;
to Shiv; to my siblings, grandparents, family, and friends for their
continuous support*

PREFACE

I am writing this book for those who want to share their stories and reclaim their lives. It is a dialogue to connect and inspire others living with kidney disease. There are no how-to books on this topic, so learning from someone else's firsthand experience may be the best source of insight available.

I have always felt compelled to share my story because what I wanted most when I was first diagnosed was to hear someone else's story—to connect with a community. I wanted to understand how my life would play out because kidney disease is life-changing. As you read this book, you will follow my journey from the point at which I was diagnosed until now. You will read about my experiences and the realizations I have had along the way. At times, I provide more context to situations so you can better understand my perspective. I hope that reading my story supports you on your journey to finding your why and connecting with your purpose. Ultimately, I want you to be able to live a full, authentic life.

My goal in sharing this extended journey is to find myself —my purpose. In doing so, I have focused on removing the roadblocks I've placed for myself over the past decade. This has helped me get connected to my *why*: my passion project called Antidote. Antidote is a platform that offers community and encouragement to patients of all ages and backgrounds who are living with kidney disease. This all-encompassing platform provides much-needed support, including connection, accountability, resources, and information to help them live longer, healthier lives.

Please join me in sharing your truth and supporting others through their experiences by visiting http://antidotehealth.io —your ally in health. It all begins by saying YES to yourSELF. Your time is now, so take it!

THANK YOU!

Grab your *FREE* well-being kit below!

https://marvelous-crafter-2297.ck.page/29361ca3e4

Manage your health and wellness with this *FREE* well-being
kit that includes a daily emotional, mental, physical, and
spiritual check-in along with a daily planner to support you in
managing your day-to-day health and overall well-being. You
deserve to take care of yourSELF!

PART I
DIAGNOSIS

CHAPTER 1

SHOCK

I am sitting in a small, sparsely decorated room, with an outdated hotel-style painting hanging from a beige-coated wall. I opted out of sitting on the blue examination chair and claimed a stool. I was never comfortable being examined, and every time I was told to sit in the blue chair, it meant the doctor was going to do a checkup. It was the summer of 2007. I rarely went to the doctor's office aside from an annual checkup, so this time I was not expecting anything different. As my mom and I sat in the room, I fell into silence. I was no longer observing the brisk movements of nurses going in and out of different patient rooms, each murmuring something as they passed each other by. I was getting nervous. I found myself daydreaming about playing tennis with my soon-to-be teammates. It was a nice summer day and there was a long, fun day of tennis practice ahead. As the doctor came into the room, I felt unsettled; my heart was racing. She was calm, reserved, and spoke hesitantly. I knew from her demeanor that what she had to say was not good. Immediately my stomach sank as she said in a regretful tone, "I am going to refer you to a friend of mine, Dr. Kuizon . . . a nephrologist at Kaiser Sunset." As she sat down, I was trying to grasp what this meant. I had never heard of nephrology.

My mom and I did not understand what she was telling us; why was I being referred to a specialist!? Earlier in the day, I had arrived with a big smile on my face because I was at the doctor's office to get clearance to play on the JV women's tennis team. I was ecstatic. I was living and breathing tennis at this point, with long rallies that lasted numerous hours in the San Fernando Valley heat. My best friend and I would take over the high school tennis court and practice the entire summer. We loved tennis—truly loved it! It was a passion we had recently discovered, and we took up the sport relatively quickly. We went from taking a tennis class as sophomores to playing on the team as juniors. I had become so enthralled that my dream was then to be a professional tennis player. I was determined to make it my reality.

So, I had walked into the office early that morning expecting to get back on the courts later that day. It was supposed to be an easy process, one I had done previously for the basketball team. I was going to be in and out in no time. I first sat to have my blood pressure read, and within seconds it came back as far too high, particularly for a healthy, athletic fifteen-year-old. The staff became alarmed. I thought that maybe I had moved during the reading or something strange had occurred, but it kept reading high. I was sent to do some blood work, and that is when things became increasingly concerning. The doctor had us stay in her office until the results came back. We were stunned when she called us back into the room to share that my results were abnormal. Something was wrong with me, and she had a general idea of what it was. I showed signs of kidney failure, but I would have to speak with a kidney specialist (a nephrologist) to understand what my body was experiencing.

I was numb. Within hours, my whole life had been flipped upside down, and now I was facing a new reality—one that contained much uncertainty. As my mom and I left the hospital, tennis was the furthest thing from my mind. The anxiety about my health appeared suddenly, like a dark cloud on a bright, sunny day.

How could I process what I had just heard? What did this mean for me and my future!? As the questions began to flood my mind, I kept replaying my bout with migraines. I had been suffering from migraines for close to a year. I had episodes lying in bed for two to three days at a time and hiding under the covers to avoid triggering myself. The light was debilitating, my senses were heightened, and I could no longer handle being around others. There were many times when I went to school, came home, and went straight to my room. I did not want to be bothered by light or sound. As time went on, the migraines began affecting my productivity and causing me to lose focus in school. I was prescribed high doses of ibuprofen to manage the pain better. For a time, I was taking at least one to two pills every other day. Once I was diagnosed with kidney disease, the migraines essentially went away. I learned that the migraines were most likely an early symptom caused by extremely high blood pressure. It had likely been high for some time since my kidney function was already down to 20% when I was diagnosed. I was in stage 4 kidney failure and my kidneys were holding on by a thread. Due to the severe high blood pressure and chronic kidney disease, I started recording my blood pressure readings throughout the day. Every day, it would read something like 240/140. These readings were extremely alarming, as they were high enough to potentially cause a heart attack. I was terrified, and I could not understand why my body was attacking itself.

As the week went on, I got back to practicing tennis with friends. Tennis was my escape. When I played, I was focused and at peace. However, there was a lingering uncertainty in my mind, and I could not shake the anxiety about my upcoming appointment. I was nervous about visiting the nephrologist and finally getting answers. It sounds odd to say this, but I felt more secure not knowing what was truly happening to my body. As they say, "Ignorance is bliss." I wanted to ignore the reality of what was happening, for time to hold still. As we waited in the nephrologist's office, I attempted to gather my thoughts and figure out my expectations. I was drawing blanks, and my body grew tense. As the anticipation built, in walked a petite woman, nicely dressed and well-spoken. She was my first nephrologist; she was gentle, kind, and lighthearted. During the conversation that followed, she explained to me and my mom that my lab results were concerning and indicated a possible kidney condition. I tried to wrap my brain around what was said, yet I could not process the information. It was even worse for my mom, whose third language is English, trying to understand what the doctor was saying about her child's potentially severe health condition. I attempted to step in a few times to translate the information the doctor was sharing. My mom and I were both fully aware that medical terminology was a language we did not have in common with the doctor. Most of the information went over our heads. The conversation lasted less than thirty minutes. As the doctor was finishing up, she recommended that we do a kidney biopsy immediately to confirm the diagnosis, so we set up an appointment. I remember walking back to the car with my mom—neither of us speaking a word. We sat in silence while I scanned through the radio, trying to distract myself. We had instructions on what to do once I arrived home, but we needed some time to process what we had just learned. As my mom and I walked up the concrete steps to our front door, I anticipated my family asking how my appointment went. They all knew that I had an important appointment, but they did not have any details. I walked in casually, and immediately my brother and oldest sister asked, "How did it go? What did they say?" I did not know what to tell them other than the doctors scheduled a biopsy on my kidneys for the following week. They were quiet, probably in shock, because no one had expected such news. None of us knew what would happen moving forward, but we were all eager to learn the biopsy results.

When it was finally biopsy day, I wasn't sure what they were going to do. Did the procedure mean they were going to cut me open? Would they put me to sleep, or would I be awake for the procedure? Surely the biopsy would be very simple, I thought, and the procedure would take no more than an hour or two. They made a small incision on the middle right part of my back where the kidneys are located. The physician used a needle to take a tiny sample from the inside of my kidney. The sample was sent out for testing, so now we had to wait. The procedure took about an hour. I was bandaged up and sent out the door. I went straight to the courts and filled my time with hours of tennis. I shared with my best friend and tennis teacher that I had a biopsy and was awaiting the results. Till then, I was set to play along with everyone else in the upcoming matches. Within a few days, I was called to the nephrologist's office to discuss my biopsy results. The doctor shared that my results showed progressive stage 4 membranoproliferative glomerulonephritis (chronic kidney disease). I fell silent . . . dread took over my body. I was not sure if I should cry, scream, or ask, "Why me?!" The doctor explained that I had a rare disease, which progressed dramatically, and now my kidneys were on their last leg before complete failure. There are five stages of renal disease, 5 being the worst, and I was at 4 or a borderline 5. My kidney function was around 20%, and at this point, all we could do was try to sustain it as long as possible.

As my mom and I left the doctor's office, we didn't speak much. There was sadness looming in the air, covered by a layer of fear. Once we got home I shared the news with my siblings, and my mom spoke with my dad. No one knew what to say, what to do, or how to act. I had been diagnosed with something that could not be cured, and nothing could console me. My dad was the most silent; he is very traditional and doesn't share his more sensitive side. He shies away from emotions and tears, at least in front of others, because it shows vulnerability. I could see that there was sadness in his eyes, but I could not take the sadness away: not his, mine, or anyone else's.

As I reflected on my ordeal with terrible migraines the year before, it became an unhealthy fixation because I was now focused on blame. I did not have anyone or anything else to blame. Aside from the occasional fatigue and retention of fluids, I had not exhibited any other symptoms as my kidney function dropped drastically. I was suffering from a silent disease. I believe that ibuprofen could be a factor as to why I developed chronic kidney disease (CKD). This medication is harmful to the body, especially in high doses, with the main side effect being kidney failure. To this day I have no definite answers as to how I ended up with CKD. The doctors say it could be due to a genetic mutation or infection. I have worked with a geneticist, yet there is not enough research to unlock this mystery. Once we confirmed my diagnosis, the doctor recommended I go on a strict renal diet and precise medication regimen while I awaited a kidney transplant. I was fifteen—still considered a child—so a kidney transplant was my best option. Later I would find out that actually receiving a transplant from a donor list is very difficult. I've met people who waited ten to fifteen years to finally get a transplant, although the wait was due to their age (40+) and state of health. Soon after my diagnosis, my nephrologist set me up with appointments at UCLA and Cedars-Sinai to begin the process of meeting the transplant teams and adding my name to the transplant list. Honestly, I do not know how the list works, and I could never track my place on it. All I know is that children under the age of eighteen are more likely to get a transplant because youth is on their side. Since I was young, my prospects looked promising. But before all of this could occur, my family and I had an appointment with the medical team to discuss the different options for me once my kidney disease entered stage 5—complete failure. My family was asked if they would be interested in donating a kidney and were given an explanation of the extensive testing they would have to do to see if they were a match (blood type, among other things). I knew my family members were more than willing to donate a kidney to me. Still, the medical team suggested that we not make further plans yet, but instead focus on sustaining me on medication as long as possible because hopefully, it would be my turn for a transplant.

CHAPTER 2

ANGER

My parents, who had always been my protectors, were helpless. As the days went by, we did not speak about my diagnosis. Everyone went into "savior" mode and tried to help me create a new sense of normal. I had already begun an extreme renal diet, which restricted my potassium, phosphorus, and sodium intake. I was told that I should remove all of those minerals in my diet, which is *extremely hard*! Just about every food contains those minerals. I was shocked by my limited options and soon felt the effects of not being able to eat freely. I was angry, frustrated, and overwhelmed by what I was experiencing. What the hell was I supposed to eat, and how could I still function? I thought that I would end up being skin and bones. I was 5'9", 120 pounds, and quickly losing weight. My mom shared my concerns, so she got creative with my diet. She would give me cereal in the morning with almond milk and a teaspoon of fish oil. It sounds gross, but it did not taste too bad. We were working with a minimal selection, and being vegetarian left us with even fewer options. I mainly had Indian chai and roti (an

Indian tortilla) for breakfast with rice and curry at least once a day as my main meal. In addition to figuring out the diet, I was always stressed. I was still a teenager trying to understand how this diagnosis would affect the trajectory of my life. I had many plans for my upcoming junior year of high school, such as the tennis team, school dances, and parties. Suddenly, I experienced the grief of moving on from the only life I had known. I now had to show up differently and change my priorities to ensure that I would survive. My life was at stake, and I could not allow myself to go through a complete breakdown because it was time to take action. All I would think about was, "Am I going to die? I do not want to die young. There is so much I still want to experience." The fear-based narrative around death took over my thoughts for the next several years, and I was unable to snap out of it. I honestly did not know what the future held for me. There was a period, for about a year after I was diagnosed with CKD, that I was fearful of dying in my sleep from a heart attack due to high blood pressure. That thought was always running through my mind, and I could barely focus on anything else. My parents recognized that I was struggling with something. The dark under eye circles, uneasiness, and tension were very apparent. I would come downstairs around 1 or 2 p.m. every day since I wouldn't go to bed until around 8 a.m. There were many days that I cried myself to sleep. I became crippled with fear, and my frustration grew with my insomnia. I could no longer sleep at night. After many days of contemplation, I could not take it anymore. My body was failing me, and I wanted support. One afternoon, as my parents conversed over lunch, I came down the stairs after another frustrating night. I was fatigued beyond measure, and I could not continue to fight this battle alone. As I sat there and shared my struggle, my parents became very worried because I had been managing this fear in silence. As they slept peacefully in bed my mind would race, and all I wanted was to run to their room as my heart beat uncontrollably. However, I would second-guess myself over the fear of judgment and embarrassment. Anyone reading this might easily say I was too old to be afraid to sleep alone at night, but this was my reality. I became so debilitated by the fear that when my parents asked if I wanted to sleep in their room, I immediately said yes! Their gesture was exactly what I needed. I wanted someone to watch over me. Every night around 10 p.m., I would grab my blanket and pillow and walk the twelve feet from my bedroom to theirs. I would prepare a makeshift bed on their bedroom floor and attempt to sleep. The new sleeping arrangement did not, by any means, eliminate my fear; however, I felt a little better being around my parents. I was still debilitated to the point that I forced myself to stay awake at night while everyone else was sound asleep. My theory was that if I had a heart attack while everyone else was asleep, then no one would help me. I wanted to make sure someone watched over me while I slept, so I began to shift my sleep schedule to daytime. I would sleep on the couch in my parents' living room and eventually created a base for myself there.

It has taken me many years to finally overcome the fear of sleeping alone. I still suffer fear-inducing moments, but I have learned to reframe my thoughts to better support me. I focus on my health by reassuring myself that my body is healthy, and my kidney transplant is doing well. It is still possible that I could lose my transplant and face dialysis, another transplant, or death. So, to avoid living in a state of fear, I am learning to accept the possibility of death. As I dealt with the fear of death, I also succumbed to the fear of uncertainty. I had no control over my health outcome, so it was difficult to plan for the future. I tried to focus my energy on more positive things to distract my mind. I turned my attention toward making progress in other areas of my life by getting a driver's license and enrolling in college courses. However, as I reflected and contacted my close friends, I would immediately see myself as "other." I wanted to belong by living a "normal" life, and I could not accept my new reality. I was in denial for many years; I thought that if I tried harder then people would see me as one of them, not as different. This was when I began to compare myself to others, and you will see this pattern continue throughout different stories I will share.

As I was adjusting to my new reality, the summer passed. I had to manage my medications, taking 20+ pills on schedule at different times of the day. I also had to develop meals that worked with my limitations yet were still somewhat nutritious. It was a demanding regimen. I took three Renvela three times a day with my meals, in addition to Epogen shots, sodium bicarbonate, Lasix to remove excess fluids, Cozaar, Clonidine, Lisinopril, and the most dreadful, Kayexalate to reduce potassium. I spoke with my tennis teacher and shared my story with him. He was very supportive and understood that I could no longer be a part of the tennis team. I wanted to continue playing, but my energy was low, my body was tired and weak, and my health was my priority. It was now time to start my junior year of high school. At this point, very few of my friends knew what I was experiencing, and now I was having to continually relive my summer. As others were sharing what they had done—family vacations, swimming, going to the mall to hang out with friends—I was unsure of what to say. Should I speak the truth, or should I only talk about the parts of my summer that did not relate to having kidney disease? I attempted to create a more relatable narrative for myself, but the circumstances of my health became undeniable. While I enjoyed my classes and spending time around my peers, my body could not keep up with my mind. I had retreated within myself, distancing myself from friends and family—no longer social. At that point, I shared with my teachers and a few peers what I was experiencing, and they all showed empathy. At one point, they wrote me letters, and in my Spanish class, they gave me a Build-a-Bear teddy bear filled with encouraging and supportive messages. The gestures were all sweet and much appreciated, but for some reason I could not connect with my emotions. It was as if I was afraid that if I showed emotion, I would open a floodgate that I would not be able to shut again. I was fragile, holding myself together by a thread. I had difficulty sleeping, activities no longer interested me, and I spent a lot of time lying around. Due to this inconsistency and inability to maintain a schedule, I decided to pursue homeschooling. At the time, one of my dear friends had recently discovered a homeschooling center and enrolled to complete her high school credits through this program. It was and still is a non-traditional way of learning for most kids, but I figured this was the most suitable option for my lifestyle. I am an inquisitive and active person who enjoys many things, including academics. I was doing very well in school and wanted to continue to do so, but the absences and lack of focus affected my grades. One day, I finally built up the courage to speak with my mom and ask her if she would support me in transitioning to homeschool. It was the first time she had heard of such an institution, which did not require her or anyone else to teach me. The coursework is self-taught. I would learn at my own pace and be tested in a well-structured environment that would keep me on track with students in a traditional educational setting. The structure of the program made my mom comfortable enough to give me the go-ahead in order to make the transition.

I visited the Opportunities for Learning (OFL) homeschooling center with my oldest sister and gained all of the information necessary to enroll. The next step was to unenroll at my high school. In a matter of ten to fifteen minutes, I would no longer be a student among thousands of other students at my local high school, one that my cousins, sisters, and brother attended and graduated from; however, I was excited about this new chapter. I had found a community that was supportive and flexible with my circumstances. I got a signed letter from my mom and drove myself to school. I walked through the hallway lined with lockers; it was a stark reminder of the drastic difference in my life that I had experienced over the past six months. As I walked to the administration office, I became nervous about what would come next. I handed the administrator the form, and just like that, I was no longer a Chatsworth High School student. I could not have been happier about the decision I made. Let me say that *homeschooling is incredible*—at least that was my experience of it. I had a super-flexible schedule and would only take a test on a subject upon completion. That meant I had plenty of time to lounge around, sleep in, go to all of my medical appointments, and most importantly, heal my body. I taught myself all of the subjects via textbooks and homework packets, which I did well with. I was finishing work quickly and felt the need to take on a more considerable challenge, so I enrolled in my first college class. I had already earned my driver's license so that I could attend college and chauffeur myself to my medical appointments. I started reconnecting with my closest friends, who appreciated my new driver's license, and we would go around exploring the city. It was a fun time; I was thriving and accelerating faster than I had expected. It was now senior year for my friends, and I was close to completing my senior year homeschooling. My friends were discussing things like prom, homecoming, and grad night. In the past, we had imagined doing these things together, but now, as the milestones arrived, I was watching from the sidelines. I was still connected with my friends, but I was technically not allowed to join in on the fun since I was no longer a student at that school. I tried not to give these moments too much thought since that would only upset me, knowing that my friends were at a different place in their lives than I was. However, I did get a chance to attend grad night. It was an exciting evening and a wonderful opportunity to be among my friends, creating memories we had dreamed about in the past. Kids were drinking, sneaking in weed, and dabbling in other things, and that was when I noticed the difference between my life and the lives of the other seventeen-year-olds around me. Being exposed to and seeing everyone be wholly free and act with passion was not something I could relate to. They were young and carefree while I was young, careful, and limited. At least that was how I felt since I was not wise enough to know that it was all a matter of perspective and that I was viewing my life from a limited lens. I became attached to a new narrative that I was incapable of performing at the same level as others. I would be sick, alone, and limited. I was now looking down the barrel of a yearslong battle with depression and anxiety.

CHAPTER 3

GRIEF

I felt more and more confused about what my life would look like in six months, let alone in a year or more. I was now just a few months shy of my high school graduation. My friends were talking about college, and I was also considering which university to attend. I did not feel comfortable or stable enough to thrive at a university that was not close to home. I was still stabilizing my health with medications, and I did not yet feel comfortable leaving my family and friends behind—the people that understood me and my circumstances. There was also another thing on my mind: boys. Yes, I was thinking about boys, just like other teenage girls. My friends were experiencing dating, and some had entered their first real relationships, not just the "one-week flings" to show off in front of others. I had been approached by guys and asked out on dates before leaving high school, but I had yet to find someone that I was interested in. Once I left the traditional high school, my opportunities to be around and connect with boys my age were very slim. There were the occasional attractive guys in my college classes, but I was way too nervous and shy to approach them, and I would limit any opportunities for them to approach me. I was insecure and having CKD did not boost my confidence. If I were to find someone that I was interested in, how would I connect with them without eventually having them experience my life with CKD? It was part of my day-to-day life in almost everything I did: limiting what I ate, taking medications, feeling fatigued, and always being in and out of the hospital. And besides all of these thoughts, it got worse when one day my parents came to my room, sat on my bed, and started in on me about the topic of marriage. It was odd for them to approach me at the same time, so I felt uneasy. As they sat, I turned to look at them briefly before tending to my closet again. As I organized my closet, they slowly began the uncomfortable, unexpected conversation of what my life would look like from this point forward, namely who would take care of me, what would become of me, and last but not least, who would marry me? Or would I even be marriage material? Well, they did not want to say this, but in their traditional Indian minds, they believed that my potential marriage partners would be limited to those who had a similar, if not the same, medical condition. Having an arranged marriage is a very prominent part of Indian culture, and there is a ranking of criteria from ideal to least ideal when looking for a partner. There is less emphasis placed on such criteria in American culture, but people still create a list of what they seek in a partner. I also presumed that they mentioned the topic of marriage because they wanted to share with me what they deemed was a significant concern: me finding a partner that I could settle down with and build a stable life with. They would be there for me always, but before my diagnosis they had thought that marriage was definitely in my future, and now they were not so sure. I remember this conversation very vividly because it was shocking, upsetting, and shifted my mindset for the subsequent decade. When they contemplated these questions, it made me angry. I was upset and, at the same time, extremely heartbroken. I understood why my parents asked me about it; they themselves are in an arranged marriage, and many things were considered before matching them—one of the major considerations being health. I just stood there and tried to gather the words to respond. I felt like I was not given a chance to prove myself or show that I am more than a health condition. Marriage should be the least of my parents' concerns; their priority should be my health and happiness. As they continued to talk, I responded in very few words. I could feel my throat closing. I was choking on words, and tears were about to run down my face. I did not want to be vulnerable in front of them and show my emotions; otherwise, they might feel pity toward me. I continued to listen as they stated, "We want you to know that we are here for you and will take care of you for the rest of your life. You do not have to worry or feel that you will be a burden on someone else. We will take care of you. It may be difficult for you to get married unless you find someone like yourself (someone else with CKD), who could be considered 'on the same level' in life." My interpretation of this was, "No one else would consider marrying you because your health is too great a burden to bear." In an Indian family, parents typically have a significant influence on who their child chooses as a marriage partner. The considerations include what their family does for a living, what the partner does for a living, their health, financial stability, ability to have children (something I will discuss later), age, education level, and so on and so forth. It is a very daunting task in the face of all this to be optimistic and continue the search for a compatible partner.

Once the conversation ended, my mind was flooded with thoughts, mainly negative. I sat down in my room as dread took hold of me. I imagined myself as a forty-year-old living with my then elderly parents in a small backhouse built by them to give me the illusion of privacy and independence. Perhaps I would have a dog or two to keep me company if my health was still good and I could stay active. I might have a few friends but would probably not be very comfortable socializing with others my age because they would all be married or with a partner and most likely have kids—all the things I wanted for myself. I would feel depressed about not traveling or living a purposeful and passionate life, as well as guilty for being a burden on my parents and family. This was the story I created for myself. It was time for me to choose my reality. I decided I was going to do all the things that people thought were not possible for me. I would create some distance from my loved ones so that they could view me through a different lens: one that was independent, enthusiastic, joyful, optimistic, carefree, and in most people's eyes—ideal. This way of living, I believed, could only be done if I chose to hide my condition and shut off that part of my reality from others. I closed off a piece of myself to be accepted, be like everyone else, and prove others wrong.

PART II
DISCOVERY

CHAPTER 4

REALITY

I went about my life as best I could and continued to pursue my next steps. I had continued to home school while using my free time to explore the environment around me and pursue tennis. I was still very passionate about tennis and believed that taking care of myself while building up my game would eventually allow me to play professionally. I had a dream and I was going to pursue it. I had met my private tennis coach when my friend and I were playing at the local park one day. He saw my talent and offered me the opportunity to join one of his classes. I was more interested in private lessons, which would give me more time to learn the techniques that would push me up the ranks once I began competing. I met with him three mornings a week, which was about the only thing I would wake up for before 11 a.m. Tennis gave me a sense of self. I had opened myself up to a new sport not long before my diagnosis; however, post-diagnosis, I leaned on my newfound passion to support me through the healing. It was the first step to reclaiming my life. My parents were very supportive and encouraged me to play tennis because they saw the joy it brought to my life. It gave me confidence and provided the catalyst to get me feeling good again. I heard about the BNP Paribas Open, a nearby tournament where I could see all of the biggest stars. Being in that environment could give me perspective, so I pursued opportunities to participate in the tournament. I noticed that there were some volunteer positions open, so I applied. I heard the great news that I was accepted. The next thing I remember was my parents driving me to a family friend's house in Indio, CA, which was where I would stay for the next two weeks (the duration of the tournament). I was on a high from experiencing such high-quality talent right in front of me. The energy of the stadium had me wanting more than I could offer. I had fallen for the game at a time when my life could have been dedicated to eating, sleeping, and breathing tennis. It was a radical mind frame compared to who I was at the time, and now I had to redefine my reality as I watched as a spectator rather than a player. I was holding on to something that could no longer be my priority. Each time I was reminded of tennis, I found myself trying to hold on to my old reality. But I could never go back to my old reality. It was time to claim my new reality—my health.

As I began to embrace my new reality, I gained confidence in taking action and going after my goals. I wanted to continue college and obtain a four-year degree, so I began taking more courses at the local community college. I had taken a magic and witchcraft anthropology course as one of my first classes, which inspired me to pursue a degree in anthropology. I enjoy learning about different cultures and human behavior. While I was growing up, my parents placed a huge emphasis on my three siblings and me pursuing at least a four-year degree, but that began with us excelling in K–12. My parents are not college educated. My mother had the opportunity to finish high school, but my father had a middle school education. We did not come from a family of highly educated, academically focused, sought-after professionals. It was instilled in us to do well for ourselves, and opportunities were provided that could eventually lead to becoming doctors, lawyers, or engineers. The specialty did not matter, only that we pursued a prestigious career, which (they thought) would bring happiness both to them and to us. I have always had a free-spirited mentality and found ways to challenge societal norms, but the pressure of doing right by my parents prompted me to pursue the kind of career that they desired for me. Furthermore, I wanted to fit in by having others see me as capable and successful so that they would have great things to say about me instead of focusing on my health and circumstances. I did not want to be associated with my health condition. Therefore, I decided to make my parents happy by following their dreams for me, which led to my enrolling in political science courses. At one point, when I was sick and did not have much entertainment, I found myself lying on a couch and watching hours upon hours of news on CNN. I was *obsessed*! I discovered that I had an interest in politics and government, so I decided to go that route. I had always wanted to join the CIA as an agent because being a spy or analyst sounded mysterious, and the inherent risk seemed thrilling and exciting. This pursuit ended when I got diagnosed with CKD since CIA agents cannot have serious health conditions—it is too risky. I would not have the opportunity to be an agent, but I could still pursue a law degree and work in the DC area. As I was completing my senior year of high school at Opportunities for Learning, I looked forward to expanding my horizons. I had completed my junior and senior years of high school in one year and was finished by the end of December 2008. I had taken the SAT in hopes of starting college in the fall of 2009. I wanted to go to college and experience the "Freshman 15", go to frat parties, live on my own, potentially find young love, and make new friends. This was all possible, but I quickly realized that I was not mentally prepared to be away from home. I enjoyed the comfort of being close to my family and the freedom to do as I pleased (within reasonable limits). I had also been attending a great local community college for a year, and I was happy to continue there. I was hesitant to participate in my OFL high school graduation, but I went anyway. It was odd to be there because I only knew one person in my graduating class. I was practically celebrating the accomplishment with strangers. My sister and mom were there to support me, and it was very emotional. I became overwhelmed with joy for having made it this far and surpassing everyone's expectations. However, I also felt profound sadness about not having my friends or teachers from my old high school around.

I put those emotions away and continued to stride forward. I felt healthy: my blood pressure readings were good, I was active, and my mind was clear. I was doing well, and my parents had just bought me a new car for graduation. I appeared to be a typical teenager with random woes and nonsensical drama. I was turning eighteen, which is a big milestone, but I was not going to have a large or extravagant party. I had disconnected from my previous life and wanted to start anew. Instead of having a party, I chose to enjoy the opportunity to visit Catalina Island with my older sister, Binaka. Before the trip, I was introduced to a new nephrologist, Dr. Hashmi, who I had been hesitant to meet but turned out to be the *best*. I was fortunate to be under his care because he genuinely cares for his patients. I knew my life mattered to him, and he would take it very personally if anything happened to me. By my definition, I was on top of my health and taking my medications, except for one disgusting medication called Kayexalate, which was mud-like in texture, color, and taste. It is everyone's least favorite, but it is an essential medication for lowering potassium levels. As I have stated before, potassium is in almost every food, so my diet would always contain some "unintentionally" consumed potassium. My entire family knew that I had difficulty taking this medication and encouraged me to focus on the effect it had on my body. However, I will admit that there were times I skimped on or skipped it altogether. Eventually, this led to trouble. One day I was at my monthly visit with Dr. Hashmi, and he pulled up my results. Every month I would get lab work done a week before my appointment, and we would discuss the results. I was sitting there talking to him while he read the results, and he turned and said to me, "Your potassium levels are extremely high. I've only seen these levels in people who are about to have a heart attack. You could have a heart attack at any moment." Hearing this was shocking, but I thought I had not done anything that bad. It wasn't like I had gotten drunk and ended up in the ER due to high levels of potassium and abnormal creatinine. He immediately told me that he was going to call my parents. I was shocked and a bit embarrassed because I had been managing my healthcare myself for the past year or so, and now Dr. Hashmi was going to out me by saying I had not been doing a good job. I sat next to him as I dialed the number then handed him the phone. My parents were surprised to hear from him because they had expected me to take care of my health, and they were disappointed to hear this news. As they spoke, Dr. Hashmi questioned their intentions and parenting skills. He asked why they had stopped taking the initiative in managing my health and preventing me from destroying myself. However, this had been my doing more than theirs. I had taken my health into my own hands around the age of seventeen. After my diagnosis, I had realized the toll it takes for parents or other caregivers to be responsible for an individual's health. My mom was one of my biggest pillars of support. She saw me during my most vulnerable moments but always showed grace and empathy through my highs and lows. She had always been by my side. She cooked for me every single day, picked up my medications, drove me to every doctor's appointment, and helped me recover after every procedure. She sacrificed herself to prioritize my health. She was my lifeline, and without her I would not have progressed in regaining my health so quickly. I felt immensely grateful for my mom's commitment to me and my health. I wanted to relieve her from taking responsibility for my health to ensure she first took care of herself.

One day I had approached my mom in the kitchen as she was cooking lunch. She asked me about my upcoming nephrology appointment, and I said, "Mom, I think I will be fine attending doctor appointments alone." She paused. I saw the bewilderment and worry drain the blood from her face. I wanted her to be confident in my ability to take responsibility for my health. I attempted to ease her nerves by telling her that I would update her after each visit. I know it was unexpected. I do not think either one of us had considered that there would be a time when I was on my own. I am sure that any parents would feel concerned about not managing their teenage child's health. To some, my parents' actions may sound irresponsible, but I became empowered to understand my disease due to this decision. I did not want to be dependent on my caregivers (my parents) to manage my health. Taking my health into my hands helped me step out of a victim mindset and become my own advocate. It was a huge decision that positively impacted my life. After Dr. Hashmi hung up, he brought a wheelchair over to where I was seated and said, "I am taking you to the ER."

I was embarrassed. Why was I being wheeled into the ER during what I thought would be a routine follow-up appointment? To combat the high potassium levels, I was given the nasty, mud-like medication (Kayexalate), along with fluids. I sat there for a few hours, contemplating my life, not realizing that my family didn't know I was in the ER. At some point, a nurse came and said, "Your sister called and would like to speak with you." My family had been trying to reach me, but I had no service. My parents wanted to find out what was going on, but I had not gotten their calls. They grew worried and began to search for me. Eventually they found me in the ER. I told them that I was fine and would be leaving soon to head back home. I was in the ER by myself and drove home shortly after potentially facing death. It was a very melancholy feeling.

I did this because I did not want to burden my family. They were in San Diego, helping my older sister Binaka move to college at the University of California, San Diego (UCSD). This was a time for them to enjoy sending their child off to college and my sister deserved to enjoy this part of her journey. My sister needed them, and I did not want my situation to rob her of her joy. My stint in the ER placed some worry on them, but luckily, I could ease their minds, so they did not have to rush to my rescue. I carried a lot of guilt over my parents and siblings. My parents were trying their best to care for three other children who still needed their love and attention. I felt like I was already taking more than my share, so I did not want to deprive them of more. This is one example of the story I created of being a "lone wolf," always focusing on myself because I did not want to rely on others for support. In my eyes, it was easier to face life alone. If people got too involved, they would get hurt, and I did not want to be responsible for their feelings. As I would learn, at some point we must realize that we are not responsible for other people's feelings; that is something they are responsible for, and we cannot control it. After this incident, I tried to make more conservative decisions about my health, but the teenager in me still gave my doctor and parents some headaches. I was strong-willed, stubborn, and wanted to be in control.

The new school year was about to begin, but I was already ahead due to having graduated early, so I considered attending FIDM (Fashion Institute of Design & Merchandising). I enjoyed fashion, styling in particular, and I thought it would be an excellent creative outlet as well as a potential career. I asked my parents about pursuing it, but they were a bit doubtful in regard to what I would gain from the program. They decided it would be in my best interest to focus on a four-year program and stay ahead, so I did. The first day of the new semester was exciting. I had all of the courses I wanted, and I was looking to make new friends. There was an Indian girl a few rows down from me in my Middle East political science class. I had not had many Indian friends growing up since my parents did not place us in a religious school and only required us to attend mandir (temple) during major holidays. We had freedom in choosing our beliefs—to a certain extent—but I had never felt inclined to connect with others who shared a similar background. Once I began college, however, I grew curious about the positive aspects of having friends with a similar cultural background, so I made an effort to build such friendships. The girl in my class seemed shy, subdued, and kept to herself, so I took the initiative to be an extroverted, confident personality who would strike up a conversation. Eventually we struck up a friendship, which led to many wonderful, lifelong memories.

As I began to create new social connections and expand my growth, I had new realizations. For example, one day I was being talkative and rude in my political science class and was called upon by my professor to answer a question. I immediately got defensive and chose to react disrespectfully, saying that I should not be asked to answer since I already had an A in the course and knew the answer. My response was an utterly arrogant move that I regret to this day. Upon reflection, I realized that this was an attempt to be popular and get noticed by acting rebellious. As a child, I had rebellious tendencies, but as I got older, and especially after my diagnosis, I had become more subdued and withdrawn. So, once I felt like myself again, I tried different ways of presenting myself to others to see how they would respond to me. In a sense, I did not understand how to make friends in light of my new circumstances, so this was a means for me to "get out there" and take the initiative.

As time went on, I understood the importance of friendship, vulnerability, and authentic connection, which I will touch on later. The support of friends was helpful during this time in my life because although I was learning to live a somewhat typical college lifestyle (with a few differences, such as not drinking, smoking marijuana, or underage partying), none of my friendships were dependent on those things. I felt joyful and optimistic that great things were on the horizon for me.

CHAPTER 5

GRATITUDE

As my first year of college drew to a close, I was looking forward to a summer trip to Puerto Rico! My oldest sister, Hina, had invited Binaka and me to join her and her friends for a nice tropical vacation that happened to fall close to my nineteenth birthday. I had not traveled in a few years, so I jumped at the opportunity to have some fun. I recently had my monthly visit with Dr. Hashmi, and he had shared that my kidney function had decreased since my last visit. It was the first indication that I was close to complete kidney failure (<15%). He was becoming more and more concerned about my taking the next step—dialysis. Because of this decline, I was referred to a coordinator to prepare for dialysis by choosing what form of dialysis would work best for my lifestyle. I was grateful to have a choice; I chose peritoneal dialysis. I was nervous yet hopeful that peritoneal dialysis would allow me to continue living my life with as little disruption as possible. It would also give me the freedom to still travel and enjoy my days without having to be tied down by the other option of hemodialysis, which requires a much more elaborate machine multiple times a week at a specific location. I was feeling good, so I was saddened to hear that my body was experiencing the opposite. I settled into denial. After sharing the news with my family, I became frustrated and angry. I was not ready, and how dare Dr. Hashmi ask me to make a choice sooner than I wanted! I wanted to stretch this process out as long as possible, so I told Dr. Hashmi (in a frenzied conversation) that I would not be having surgery before going on vacation. This meant that the procedure would have to wait until the end of the summer, which he was by no means happy with. He told me that I was one of the most hardheaded patients he had ever had because I was always giving him pushback on everything. For some reason I could not accept my reality, so I tried to manipulate and create my own with the very little freedom I had. At the end of the day, it was my decision, and that helped comfort me. So, I scheduled the surgery for the week after I returned from Puerto Rico.

Once I was on vacation, I had a sense of peace and calm that enabled me to let go of my worries. Experiencing Puerto Rico left me in a mindset of acceptance for the upcoming surgery. I came back full of energy and beautiful memories that I will cherish forever. The day of surgery soon arrived. I would be under the knife for a few hours and was warned that there would be some downtime and discomfort after the procedure. Once I was home, I endured severe pressure and tenderness on my belly. My core was extremely limited in movement, and all I could do was lie around helplessly; however, my family was very supportive and tended to my needs. Binaka was especially helpful post-surgery with cleaning me up and keeping me comfortable to manage my recovery. She went above and beyond and did not hesitate to step in when things got gross. She never hesitated to clean my open wounds, give me sponge baths, or wipe me after using the restroom. I felt grateful to have a caring sister who truly wanted to comfort and heal me. She saw me raw and vulnerable and never once had it in her heart to feel anything but love, compassion, and grace. For that moment and many more, I am grateful for the relationships I have with my entire family. There is a deep understanding of community and support in rallying around a loved one, which is beautiful. Their love is vast and eternal, and I know that the strong bonds I have with my family and tribe will get me through anything.

Post-surgery was a bit difficult as my muscles were sore from the catheter placement by my stomach. It was not the most appealing look and did affect my confidence, but I was looking forward to being trained to start dialysis at home, which would take place ten to twelve days after surgery. It was a time for me to reflect and come to accept the next step in my journey. A few days into my recovery, I got a call. I mean *the call*! It was UCLA Medical on the phone, calling to say that a kidney was available, but there was one person ahead of me. They had called to give me a heads-up to be ready to come in for surgery if the person ahead of me did not return their call within the next few hours. This was an extremely time-sensitive matter. If you do not answer the call, you could potentially lose your opportunity to get life-saving surgery. I was in shock! I was excited but also very nervous because I might not get a call back to come in. What would happen if the person ahead of me got the transplant? Where would that leave me? I was on edge. I told my family, and they began to prepare as much as possible, but they too were jumpy because the decision was out of our hands. As we waited, pacing back and forth, the transplant coordinator called and shared that the person ahead of me had gotten in touch with them and was preparing for surgery. I was completely devastated. When would it be my turn? I was heartbroken over the yearned-for chance to start anew but knew that I was already on a path to another option, so I should still be grateful. Another day or two passed and life settled down, and then we got *the call*! Wait, *the call!?* Is this real!? How did I get a call again within such a short time, and was this another call to tell me that I was not first in line but second? I was confused and anxious. As the coordinator began to talk, she stated that I was first in line, and my family and I had about ten hours to reach the hospital and prepare for surgery or they would give the transplant to someone else. It was an urgent call—brief, yet *so powerful*. It was life-changing! I said, "We will be there within the hour, so do not worry about calling anyone else." There was no way that I would forgo this opportunity; no one in their right mind would. We were not going to take any chances. I got off the phone and went on autopilot. I do not think any of us spoke about the actual call; we just went into preparation mode and got on the road. It was my parents and me off to UCLA Medical. Hina was living in Texas at the time, so we told her to book the first flight out and come straight to the hospital. The transplant surgery was not only an experience for me but also my entire family. As I was being prepped at the hospital, everyone around me was so calm and did their work with such flow and ease. Was I the only nervous one here? I did not know what to expect, nor did anyone prepare me for what was ahead. The nurses and doctors made their rounds to have me sign the paperwork, get me dressed in a gown, and start the IVs. As I lay in bed, ready to be hauled away into surgery, it all seemed surreal. I had always imagined more time to be present in the moment, but it all went by quickly. I had a chance to say goodbye to my parents. They were right by my side as I was pushed down the hall for surgery. I had a nervous smile on my face, holding back tears of joy and worry. The thought went through my mind of this being my last moment, the last time I would see my parents. It was apparent that we were all nervous, scared, anxious, and fearful of the unknown. My parents are not the demonstrative type, but we all felt what we could not verbalize. I saw the worry in their faces as they attempted to be strong for me. They held back their emotions, knowing that a high-risk surgery is something no one can prepare for. I wanted to be strong and trust the journey that was ahead. This was my mindset pre-surgery, and it remained so post-surgery. I always felt that I had to be strong for my family and hold it together since I was their "weak point" or point of vulnerability. As I entered the operating room, I saw an open, clean, and relatively sparse space. I was surrounded by a few nurses and doctors, who transferred me to another bed. As the anesthesiologist began to put me under, he asked, "What is your name?" I could hear ice breaking in the background (ice was used to keep the live kidney cool for my surgery), soft music, and lighthearted conversation among the surgery team. As I attempted to respond with my name, I drifted off to sleep. Hours later, I was awake, hearing the sounds of the machines and the nurses telling me that the surgery had gone well. It was such a pleasant sight! I couldn't believe what had just happened. Within hours, I had undergone a life-transforming surgery; it was an intense mental, physical, and emotional experience. I wanted to be up and running (figuratively speaking), and I was looking forward to some activity. I soon realized that I was attached to a few different machines, and my stomach was sore. I was connected to a machine that monitored my fluids and vitals throughout the day. I had an IV attached to my neck, which was an internal freak-out moment for me. I have always been very wary of needles, IVs in particular, which did not get more manageable over time, even though I was poked and prodded quite often. I had a tube poking out of the side of my stomach with blood coming out of it. As I moved, I immediately felt discomfort from the catheter in my bladder, which I thought was somehow going to leak urine all over my bed. The throbbing on my abdomen's right side was very present to me. I had not realized where my transplant was placed until I examined my incision. The surgeon shared that he had cut through my abdomen's muscles to transplant the new kidney. I had no control over my recovery time, but it was crucial to pay attention to my body and allow it to heal naturally. As I became acquainted with my environment, I began to feel the joy of what this time meant for me. My parents, siblings, grandparents, cousins, aunts, uncles, and friends were all coming in and out of my room, and it was so nice to feel their love and support. I appreciated talking to my loved ones and having some laughs (which were great but slightly painful)! I was told to eat all I wanted because now I was not restricted to a renal diet. The doctors and nurses encouraged me to eat plenty of the food I enjoyed so I would have a natural bowel movement—one of the main signs doctors look for before releasing you from the hospital. My immediate thought was, "Wait—I can eat whatever I want!? Is this true? What should I eat?" I had craved so many things at the beginning of my renal diet, but I had eventually become accustomed to the restrictions. I had not consumed cheese, french fries, whole milk, or a banana in years. My eyes lit up. I had a smile on my face, but I was hesitant to make a request. I paused because I still imagined that I would be hurting my body by eating such things. I was thinking of the circumstances in my past, but they were no longer part of my future. Before I said a word, Hina chimed in and said, "I know what you want. Let's get you some french fries." My dad dashed to the cafeteria downstairs. Within minutes he was back, french fries and ketchup in hand. As I took my first bite, I said, "This is salty!" I had not consumed so much salt in years! It tasted as if I had just eaten a spoonful of salt. It was a funny experience. Such a moment could be viewed as trivial, but for me it signified a new beginning, a rebirth. This experience was one of many firsts that I would have with food. As I adjusted to the taste of a regular diet, it became natural for me to enjoy food again. However, I was not yet active. It was two days before I took my first few steps. I was overwhelmed by the entire experience and just wanted to sleep. On the third day after surgery, I was given a wet bath, meaning that I literally took a bath while seated in a chair. It was the best bath *ever* and really boosted my spirit. The bath gave me the encouragement I needed to get up and go for a brief walk. I was now focused on exercise to regain my strength and be discharged from the hospital. It was not an easy task, but I went for short walks through the wards multiple times a day with the nurses' encouragement.

As the days passed, my medical team's visits gave me motivation and assurance that I was doing well. My social worker visited me as my discharge day was inching closer. She shared some resources on recovery and asked if I had any questions before being discharged. Most importantly, she shared that my transplant was from a ten-year-old boy who had died from a seizure. I was shocked to hear how young he had been and was grateful to his family for having donated his life to touch many others, including myself. I was told that I could reach out to his family via a written letter to share my appreciation for this life-changing surgery and being given another chance to thrive. I was overcome with emotion thinking about what to say and how to show my profound gratitude in this time of grief for their son. It was complicated, but I knew that I wanted to connect with the boy's family. I later wrote them a letter during my recovery at home, which I hope to this day that they have read. I was told that once the family received the letter, it was up to them if they wanted to connect with me or not. They have chosen not to contact me, which is entirely understandable, but I still wish to meet them one day. Finally, I only had one thing left to do to get discharged: have a bowel movement. It sounds gross and is not the most pleasant thing to think about, but that was the best yet worst bowel movement I have ever had. It was the best in terms of helping me meet the standards for discharge approval (so I could finally go home), and the worst because it was *painful*! I had been on fluids and medication for days, and to top it off, the food that I consumed had left me constipated and bloated. It was now the moment of truth, so I told my mom that I would go to the bathroom and to not let me out until I was done. As I sat on the toilet, I held on to the arm rail, gripping it tightly as my stomach began to cramp. I was sweating as if I were directly under the blazing sun. At one point I heard the nurse ask my mom, "Has she gone yet?" My mom replied with a chuckle, "No, not yet, but she is trying." As I battled the bowel war, I remained determined. Finally, after thirty to forty minutes—relief! My family and healthcare team cheered and rejoiced, which sounds hilarious, but at that moment it was so genuine. The next day, I was discharged. I was excited to be headed home since I wanted to see my puppies, Sasha and Sophie (the cutest doggies *ever*—I am biased, but that's okay). I looked forward to sleeping in my bed and having a comfortable environment to move around in. It is incredible what a massive difference a change in environment can make in a person's mental health, but just getting out of the hospital can have a tremendous positive impact. As I was wheeled out, I felt the onset of nervousness and sadness about going home. I had experienced such an amazing moment in my life with loved ones and strangers, one that we all had grown closer through. I benefited from the team's comfort, and I was nervous about being off on my own. I was not sure whether I could handle it or not, but I was dedicated to my health. As I left, I recognized how my body had changed. I was leaving the hospital ten pounds lighter, which made me look malnourished and underweight. My body took up less than half of the wheelchair, which was a shocking sight. It was a bit daunting, but I figured that if I could eat whatever I wanted, then I would quickly regain that weight in no time. (Boy, was I wrong!)

Finally, I was home, enjoying being in my own space and starting to heal. At first, I could not shower or move on my own since I had to be mindful of not opening up my stitches. As I adjusted to home life, my mom supported me by tracking my medication regimen and keeping my body fueled with delicious meals. It would take some time to regain my energy, but her support gave me the boost to stay motivated. Although I had registered for college in the fall, my surgery took place only a few weeks before classes started. I did not think it would serve me to be back at school in the hustle and bustle of everything when I should be in a calm headspace to advance my healing. I decided to forgo the fall semester, knowing that it would place me behind on the schedule I had created for graduating college. As I began to adjust to my downtime, I looked forward to attending a university far from home and enjoying the college lifestyle. I wanted to experience college the same way that my friends and comrades would, so I became stuck on that vision of college for myself. I had assumed that my transplant would place me back on track to live a typical young adult lifestyle, and no one would consider me "different" if I was perfectly healthy and functioning (physically) at their level.

CHAPTER 6

JUDGMENT

As time went on, I began to apply to universities. I took the SAT during my junior year of high school, but I had never followed through with applying to colleges because I was not confident in getting accepted to a college of my choice. More than that, I had limited myself by thinking that I was not strong enough to succeed unless my family and friends were nearby. This was the story I had created for myself. We all create narratives to justify our decisions, and I had made this decision without talking it through with my loved ones. I do not regret it; everything happens for a reason. I was meant to have a different experience, but I learned to reflect and understand my ways of thinking to ensure that I make clear choices from an unanxious headspace. I had enjoyed my time at the community college and created wonderful memories there, so I was happy with that choice. I had just completed my sophomore year of college, and I was ready to apply to universities. I planned to apply to political science programs. I took a lot of history, political science, and government courses to become a lawyer or government official. I had my hopes set on UC Berkley, with UCLA as my backup option. All universities are outstanding; reflecting on it now, I realize that I was more attached to the university's name than the ideals and experience I would get there. I was so excited about the potential prospects that I ended up attending different college tours and would imagine myself immersed in the student body of each one.

It was now springtime, just a few short months before my junior year would begin. I was anticipating the acceptance letters coming any day now. The first letter that I opened was from UC Santa Barbara (UCSB)—accepted! I ran straight to my parents with a massive smile on my face, saying, "I got in!" The result put me on an optimistic high of hoping for good news from the other universities. But then I got my letter from UC Berkley (rejected). I was very disappointed and got stuck on trying to figure out why. Then a letter from UCLA arrived —another *rejection*! I was devastated. I had received a kidney transplant from their hospital; I had been there multiple times a week for months, and I knew the campus well. Out of all the schools, I had least expected this response from UCLA. I broke down in tears in front of my parents after I read the letter. I began to second-guess my intelligence. I had given this decision so much power that it paralyzed my thinking, and I could not imagine going to school anywhere else. My parents asked how they could support me. My dad eagerly responded with, "Let's go to the campus and ask to speak with the dean." My mom chimed in with an agitated tone, urging me to appeal the decision. It was lovely of them to go into problem-solving mode, but all I could feel was frustration. After a few days, I mustered up the courage to appeal the UCLA decision and was rejected again. They said that the major I had applied to was impacted, and it would better serve me to choose another major if I decided to apply again. I still had one college that I had not heard from: UC San Diego (UCSD). At last the letter came—*rejected*! I began to doubt my college potential. My spirit was *crushed*. I was losing hope, but I was still grateful for my acceptance to UCSB. I hopped on to my laptop and registered for the Fall 2011 term. At this point, I had given up on attending UCSD (even though I had appealed the decision) and was not going to look back—until I did. I got into UCSD (the school that my sister had just graduated from), and I was excited to follow in her footsteps. The college was familiar to me, and the campus was a better fit for my lifestyle. So, I unenrolled at UCSB, then enrolled at UCSD for the fall term. This was the moment I had been waiting for. My friends and I discussed where we would be moving and the experiences we most looked forward to. It was an opportunity for us to become adults and begin to shape our future lives. I enjoyed the summer but also longed for school to start. Before getting situated at UCSD, I had decided to apply to live in student housing as a transfer student with other new enrollees. I was set up with new roomies in a modern two-bedroom apartment close to ERC (Eleanor Roosevelt College). My family was excited for me, and they all came to move me into my new apartment. I was very excited to share the experience with them, so they could see me continue to pursue my dreams no matter what challenges I faced, as their support was what had gotten me this far. I was looking forward to my independence, but I was also sad not to have them nearby. Soon it was time for them to leave. Once all of us roomies had said our goodbyes, we sat down together to get to know each other a little more. We had spoken briefly before, but I was anticipating our interactions once we moved in. I was housed with a diverse group of women: a Swede (a lovely, calm, and caring soul), an Iranian (who moved to the States in her teens and was experiencing a clash of American and Iranian cultures), and a Filipina (who moved here in her teens and was in an exploration phase). I sensed that this living arrangement would go well, and I would make lifelong friends during my time there. I had shared my health condition with them at our first roomies' meeting so they would not be alarmed by the amount of medication I took and the cautions I observed as an immunocompromised person. I was on immunosuppressants (and will be for the life of the kidney), and I must be careful around others to protect my health. They didn't seem to be alarmed and took an interest in learning more about my condition rather than shutting me down about it. It was in this moment that I started feeling the need to explain myself to others. I had experienced judgment from people who assumed that I was a "druggie," and that must be why I had kidney disease. It sounds very immature and unwarranted, but this is the judgment I faced from some extended family members in India. I had become aware of this one day when I heard, through my sister, that people from my parents' state of Gujarat were talking about what had caused my kidney condition. One of these people was my mom's first cousin. I was fuming with anger. Why would people spend their time coming up with theories as to why I have CKD? I did not know what to do, so I approached my mom. It was late evening, and she was in the kitchen winding down. She was on the phone with some family members in India, so I lingered to listen in on the conversation. After she got off the call, I asked, "Why did you not say anything?" She was confused as to what I was referring to. I think she knew but did not want to argue, so she acted perplexed. As I stood there, she shared that it was best to avoid arguing and looking bad; she was about saving face, and she thought it would cause a rift with her extended family if she did say something. Also, this man was one of her closest cousins. It was sad to witness my mom not defend me, but it was more about the culture than about her. In Indian culture, it is very taboo to talk back to family or elders. It is not a very open culture to hearing others out, especially if you are a woman. Things were even less progressive at that time, and I'm sure she had difficulty being heard by the male family members in her life. As a teenager I saw the dynamics and I recognized that as an American, I was more open to speaking freely and challenging people's beliefs because I had more freedom to do so. I became very distrustful of people because I felt let down by family. I needed love and support during this time, but instead I received negative, harsh responses. It was as if I was being punished for having a medical condition. All I wanted was to be surrounded by people who could support me in overcoming this condition so that I could thrive in my circumstances. It left me feeling alone, and it tied into how I chose to get support, which in most cases, was by giving support rather than asking for it. I decided to take on life alone.

CHAPTER 7

BREAKDOWN

College was the first time for many of us to finally be away from home and on our own, it was to be expected that many kids were going to go wild. People wanted to host parties so they could drink and hook up; it was all about having a good time. We would get knocks on our door from people saying, "Hey, come down to our place tonight in Apt. 3A!" I had been to parties before; this was not new to me. As a teen, I drank on a few occasions and went to parties where my friends would drink and smoke weed. I didn't dabble in the latter, but I had my fair share of party experiences before being diagnosed with CKD.

In the spirit of socializing, I decided to go to some of these parties and see for myself what college was all about. College is about learning, not partying, but at the time I was more interested in the social aspect. Our lives play out in seasons, and I thought this would be my time for that particular season. I was anxious to go to parties and nervous about what kids might attempt to pressure me to do, but I figured I was mentally strong enough to hold my ground if such things happened. I thought that all college kids were understanding and open-minded, but I was wrong. I encountered belligerent kids who judged me the first time they saw that I was not drinking. I was offered drinks plenty of times in their attempts to get me to "fit in," but I declined. It was odd to them that I was there because if I was not drinking, how could I be having fun? At one party, I encountered a young white male who asked if I wanted a drink. I said, "No, thank you. I do not drink," and his reply was, "Oh, that is weird." I shared that I had a kidney transplant, to which he did not reply. I was taken aback—was this how he perceived me? I tried not to get stuck on what he said, but this interaction changed my trajectory and shaped many of my decisions in the coming years. I was no longer comfortable sharing my diagnosis with people because I did not want to be defined by it. I was afraid that people would base their interactions with me on my health condition. At that moment, I had experienced being different. I did not feel that I fit in; I was not "normal." I approached my roommate and asked to leave because I no longer felt welcome or comfortable being there. She understood why I was hurt, but she could not relate to me. My other roommates did not find it odd and were not bothered by what had happened. I guess I was expecting some understanding or empathy, but I was shocked to find neither. In a last-ditch effort to fit in, I decided to pledge for a sorority. Reflecting on it now, I realized that I would essentially have been paying to join an established club and gain automatic friends. The process was tedious and tiresome. I reflected on one specific question that ultimately supported my decision: Why was I waiting in long lines for hours to convince a group of women to take me into their circle and give me the acceptance that I should not be seeking among them or anyone else, but only from myself? It was an odd and unsettling feeling, so I removed myself from participating in match day. As time passed, I found my desire to participate in classes and the student body waning. I was no longer comfortable being around my peers. I became paranoid that people were speaking about me negatively and I could not engage with others. I became withdrawn and isolated. I noticed that I was coming home every weekend and leaning on my family and close friends for support. One weekend, I was at home and felt stuck. I was in my room looking at myself in the mirror and I saw sadness. It was a deep sorrow that I had not experienced before. I found myself in tears and recognized that I was no longer myself. The encounter at the party had changed me and left me in a depression. As I sat on my bedroom floor, I reached for my phone and called Hina to console me. I was sobbing uncontrollably, and in between breaths, I shared that I was depressed. She was extremely concerned and suggested that I speak to a UCSD professional to work through my emotions. I was uncomfortable sharing my mental state with others, but I took her advice and began seeing a therapist. I was thankful for my sister because she was the one person I was comfortable discussing mental health with—and I was free to do so without any judgment. I avoided discussing it with my parents or others within the Indian community because unfortunately, mental health is a taboo topic. I know this is true for many cultures, so I hope that reading my story will encourage you to open up to someone you trust so that you can get the support you deserve. I will say that starting therapy is one of the best decisions I have ever made in my life. This was the first time I had spoken with a therapist, but she created the space for me to be vulnerable and divulge more of myself. As she and I connected, I began to peel back the layers of grief from my diagnosis several years prior that I had never spoken about. My body and mind had been telling me to grieve, and only at this moment was I finally allowing myself to process that grief. We discussed the encounter I had with the young man at the party, and I realized that he had been a trigger that had unleashed a deeper unresolved issue. We recognized that my "bubble" had burst and I was no longer around people who knew me. As my therapist and I spoke more, we decided that it would best serve me to move back home and heal while being supported by my loved ones. I needed a strong support system around me and I did not have one at the university. It was one of the toughest decisions I have ever had to make, but it was one of the best for me. I had worries about disappointing my parents and guilt about not following through with my commitment; however, none of that mattered if I did not have peace of mind. As I mustered up the courage to speak with them, I reached out to Hina to discuss my decision and gain support for the upcoming conversation. She reassured me that my parents were there for us—always. That weekend I went home, running the conversation through my head multiple times over the three- to four-hour drive back to LA. When I got home, I settled in and enjoyed the evening, waiting for the right moment to speak with them. At the time, I believed there was always a time and place for everything. I now know there is no such thing as the "right time" and time is relative (it is measured differently by different people), so I now choose not to wait and analyze, but use my voice when I feel that I need to. As I worked up the courage to speak with my parents, I began a conversation with my dad and grandma in our living room. It was a more relaxed environment that invited casual conversations about college. As we spoke, I noticed my voice change and I could feel my throat closing. The tears were there and I was trying to hold them in. I wanted to be strong and firm when I spoke with my parents, so they would not doubt me or question my decision. I wanted to speak with my mom first (she's a little more approachable). If she agrees with something and is on board, then she can easily convince my dad or decide on his behalf. So, I walked into the kitchen where my mom was cooking dinner. As she hovered over the stove, I shared with her that school was not going so well. I did not feel settled living in San Diego and I wanted to move back home. She paused, and then she looked at me and asked what was wrong. She said that if I did not enjoy my major, maybe I could study another subject that would interest me. I would agree, but it did not sit right with me because I knew that I could no longer thrive in that learning environment in my current mental state. She then mentioned Hina and suggested that I consider studying business, like her. I could then use that knowledge to help support the family business. I thought that might be a good option, but UCSD, at least at the time, did not have a strong business program. They only offered economics, which for me was a definite no! We continued to talk and included my dad in the conversation. After about 20 minutes she said, "So what will you do if you move back home?" Well, that was a great question! I had not thought it through, but I knew I could attend our local university, Cal State Northridge, while living at home and studying finance. I shared my plan to transfer and they agreed! I think they were happy I came to them for support and excited that I would be back at home close to family. I was so happy! My parents could see the difference their support made and how relieved I felt as soon as I had gotten that conversation off my chest. I went upstairs and began planning to unenroll at UCSD.

I drove back to San Diego and shared with my friends and

roommates that I would be leaving once the quarter was over. They all seemed surprised, even shocked, but I had already mentally checked out of my time there. As winter break approached, I completed my applications for two local community colleges so that I could finish the prerequisites to gain acceptance to the business school at Cal State Northridge (CSUN). A short few days later, I packed up my entire room at school and loaded my car. The feeling I had driving out of the parking structure was bittersweet. I had longed for the college experience for so long, but I was attached to how it looked and had created a story around it that was not true to how I felt once I was there. It was one of the best times for most students but the worst time for me. As I got settled in at home, my spirit was optimistic about a brighter, happier future.

CHAPTER 8

BREAKTHROUGH

I was back home now and anticipated seeing my close friends, but I was inclined to reach out to one girl in particular whom I had met through a mutual friend. I shared with her that I had moved back home and planned to attend the same college as her, CSUN, starting in the fall. While I took spring and summer courses to help me get the credits I needed, I found friendship and sisterhood with this girl, Sona. She was fun, free-spirited, and we shared mutual interests. Her spirit inspired me to let go and be present to the world around me. As I gained confidence in myself, I began to look forward to my next opportunity to live a typical college lifestyle. During my first semester at CSUN, I took a full load of business classes. I was happy to finally be there and looked forward to joining a business club. Things were exciting, but every time I found myself opening up, something still held me back. I was experiencing anxiety; I was stuck in my head and could not make decisions. I was disconnected from others and was searching for people with health journeys similar to mine. I was not yet comfortable connecting with new people, who (I thought) would require me to explain myself, but I longed to connect with people who were similar to me. As a result, my anxiety became constant. It required an endless amount of analyzing and contemplating to make even simple decisions, such as going to the mall or filling up my gas tank. I was experiencing analysis paralysis and could no longer manage simple day-to-day tasks. As I have learned from my current therapist, the way to shift out of anxiety is by making a choice. In simple terms, anxiety is one or more problems in the mind. So, when you are anxious, bring to your mind an awareness of what problem or options you are grappling with. Then, make a choice to be okay with choosing an option at that moment. It does not have to be your choice forever, but you are choosing it at that moment. Each situation varies, so serious matters require more confidence in following through with a choice. If you analyze and question what you chose, then your mind will continue to stay in a spin (anxiety). This will leave you in a state of limbo, which stresses out your body and leads to inflammation. Therefore, if you have a hard time making small decisions, choose something, and resolve to live with that choice. You will be much happier for it. After my CKD diagnosis, I had experienced many episodes of anxiety, but I could not pinpoint what was wrong because I never spoke to anyone about it. In my household and with those around me, we never talked about anxiety or depression. I was completely unaware of what I was experiencing, why I was experiencing it, or how I could overcome it. I had gone to therapy for a short time at UCSD, but I was now looking to find someone through my healthcare provider. It took a few weeks, but I began the process and started therapy again. I was excited about gaining the tools to manage my overwhelming emotions. I wanted to engage with people. I would get very close to building new connections and trying new experiences, but I could not follow through. I was not present to what I was feeling in the moment but instead focused on others' opinions of me (through my lens). My thoughts were all fear-based. I told myself that my health was failing, and that was why I feared people or places. I feared talking to guys because I was afraid of being vulnerable and them potentially not liking me. I was scared to have people see me as I was. I had been living in a story that I built to keep me in that place of fear. Now that I was working with a therapist, those walls began to break down; the story was no longer available as an excuse. The feeling was debilitating. I felt paralyzed from indecision and overanalysis. Thankfully, I eventually learned that I did not have to remain stuck there. I was able to make my mind stronger by continuing to exercise choice until I built up mental stamina. In order to eventually get comfortable with making choices; I needed to keep pushing the edges of my comfort zone. Trust me, it works! We are capable of growing and creating new opportunities and experiences for ourselves. We do not know what is waiting for us on the other side.

At one of my visits to the nephrologist, I asked if he knew any other patients close to my age. I was the youngest patient he had. Most were in their forties or older, and here I was, only twenty-one. I wanted to connect with other kidney patients, so I decided to start a kidney support group. It was called Kidney Support Group of San Fernando Valley and it would meet once a month at the Calabasas Library. Dr. Hashmi placed flyers throughout the nephrology department. Every time I visited the office, my face lit up at seeing my posters everywhere. I was nervous about the turnout and had a lot of expectations around the group. I was attached to the outcome and did not want to disappoint others or myself. I asked Sona to join me for the first meeting, as I was too nervous about being alone. We waited and about four people showed. I was happy to see new faces, but disappointed at the turnout. The people who did attend were much older, so they had different support needs. I was optimistic that the group would grow, so I continued the meetings for about six months until I noticed that I could not serve the community as I had hoped. At this point, I had created a support group page on Facebook with a good following, was registered on aakp.org, and had built a new connection with the founder of a kidney nonprofit. I noticed that I desired to move on from my initial plans, so I asked Carol at Kidneys Quest Foundation for advice about combining groups and referring patients to her through my group inquiries. I realized that in-person meetings were limiting the potential for support. I had gone into this situation blindly and was not prepared to meet the group's needs. I wanted to meet more people my age, so I began exploring new options, which led me to Theresa. She and I met through a third-party organization that connects kidney patients to a mentor (a fellow kidney patient) to provide support. I heard about this organization through the National Kidney Foundation and decided to give it a chance. I was excited to finally meet someone close to my age and gain their perspective on the trials that I faced. One day I had gotten a call and it was the first of many that have led to a long friendship. Theresa and I are different in so many ways, but her courage inspired me. Our first phone call went so well that we spoke for over an hour and I eagerly scheduled another call. I got off the phone and ran to my mom to tell her that I had made a friend who also had kidney disease. I walked around the entire day smiling from ear to ear. As Theresa and I began to connect on a deeper level, we realized that we lived fairly close to each other. I could not believe this! Not only had I finally met someone who I connected with, but she happened to live close to me. How was it that our paths had not crossed before? I was excited to connect in person, but that desire was quickly shot down. According to the third-party rules, we were not allowed to share personal information, nor were we allowed to meet in person. These were rules that I was not willing to accept. I emailed the director of the third-party program about my intentions and concerns. Although she was not supportive of Theresa and I meeting in person, she could not prevent us from doing so. This predicament left me with a heavy heart. How many other people had missed out on this opportunity because they never questioned the establishment or pushed the boundaries? Eventually, I left the program, and Theresa and I built a friendship outside of it, for which I am forever grateful. I recognized a commonality between my experience with the mentor program and my support group, which lacked freedom, accessibility, and ease. This is how my passion project, Antidote, came about. Antidote (http://antidotehealth.io) is a platform that offers community and encouragement to patients living with kidney disease.

With all that I was experiencing, finding the tools to support me in overcoming certain obstacles required a therapist's perspective. I was assigned to a therapist at CSUN, who was *terrific*! She made me feel so comfortable and open that I could share anything with her with zero resistance. I looked forward to seeing her because I always left her office with a smile on my face. Many things came up during our sessions, especially trauma that had happened to me as a child. I believe that experiencing kidney disease had triggered past trauma that I was not fully healed from. I had not shared this part of myself with many people, apart from my sisters and a few close friends. I had a deep wound that I was now cleaning out. The trauma was connected to my anxiety and it would take a conscious effort to rewire the way I processed my emotions. As a child, I was innocent and carefree. I experienced joy by expressing myself, until one day, I was robbed of my joy when I was molested by someone my parents knew. This predator helped my parents by managing their property, which was also the place where we lived. On this day, it just so happened that my parents were out of town and my grandmother was at home with us children. It was dark. I had entered the kitchen to get a drink of water and walked into this predator standing in the archway of the entrance. As he looked at me and our eyes connected, he grabbed me. It was an uncomfortable sensation in the private area, and within seconds he took his hand away. I was only four years old. My body clenched up, and in a panic, I ran back to the room I shared with my sisters. I woke them up and told them what had happened. They got up and locked our bedroom door. As they consoled me, I saw the anger and sadness in their faces. I felt protected by their presence. There were still a few days left until my parents returned, but we managed to avoid contact with him during that time. My sisters and I never spoke to our parents about this encounter, but we will always remember it. I say my sisters because he preyed upon them too. Unfortunately, this was not my only encounter with trauma. A few years later, I was molested again during my time in India. My brother and I were playing with some local kids when a slightly older kid approached me and groped my private parts. I had faced this once before and immediately felt threatened. By now I was more aware of what is considered inappropriate, so I panicked, kicked the kid, and yelled at my brother to run. We ran and ran until we reached my aunt's house. I never looked back. The first person I told was my mother. She brushed it off as children getting a little out of hand while playing and said there was nothing to be concerned about. I swallowed my disappointment. I did not get the justice that my sisters and I deserved, so what was I supposed to do? Maybe if I had shared my first encounter with my mom, she would not have questioned me the second time. However, at the time and in the years after, all I could think about was that I did not have the protection and support of my parents that I needed in order to cope. I was left to heal on my own using the very few tools I had. I experienced disappointment and guilt in the years that followed. My mother's response told me that what I said did not matter. My words could not be trusted because I was a child. If my mother did not do anything, then how could I trust others in this world to have my best interest in mind and support me through difficult times? It was all very sad and daunting. As I discussed those memories with my therapist, I recognized that I had never healed from these traumas, which were the root that my anxiety was stemming from and the only way forward was to break through the guilt and trust issues so I could heal. I now understand that my mother dealt with Indian cultural influences, language barriers, and naivety in trusting others around my siblings and me. She was possibly fearful of the repercussions of taking our case to court. She did not grasp American culture and the policies that would protect us. There was so much unchartered territory involved, including cultural stigma. The unspoken rule was not to say anything—do not ask, do not tell. My parents never said that to me, but I had observed that my culture was not open-minded about these issues. As a woman I did not feel that my voice would be heard, so I shut off the part of me that wanted to be connected to the opposite sex. This part of me was vulnerable and emotional; it was to be respected as sacred and not be taken advantage of. As I began to work through these past traumas and the stories I had created for myself, I started to blossom. My personality began to show through my experiences and I began to get comfortable in my skin. I was learning to accept my CKD and not allow myself to be reduced to a label or engulfed by everything that came with it. I was on a path to defy everyone's odds and live life in alignment with my interests, whether other people agreed or not. This breakthrough supported me in my ongoing journey of self-discovery. As therapy began to impact my life, I started running low on the number of therapy sessions available to me through school. I was worried because my therapist had gained my trust, and now I was being asked to essentially stop my progress and build rapport with a new therapist. My therapist shared with me that therapy is a process; however, therapists' end goal is to support their patients by giving them the tools to sustain their growth on their own. No one should go to therapy thinking they need to be in it forever to make progress with their issues. If so, deeper problems and dependency are going on, which is unhealthy. As that began to sink in, I realized that I had done a lot of the root work on the issues I was facing, so it was time for me to practice what I had learned. This would be a process, but I had to start somewhere. I began to participate in more social activities, including a tennis course, to get back to my passion. I was engaging more with guys by allowing myself to connect versus shut down due to past misconceptions. I was pushing myself past limiting beliefs and experiencing a new sense of freedom. I had not experienced this since before my diagnosis, so it was refreshing to know that I could get back to a similar headspace. As the school year progressed, I noticed that I was losing interest in finance. I realized that I had decided to pursue this major because of my parents' suggestions for what I should be studying instead of my intuition. As I shared earlier, one of my first college classes was an anthropology course. I was drawn to the study of cultures, peoples, and languages. So, I decided to acknowledge this and made the decision to change my major again. As I moved into my senior year of college, I recognized the urge to explore new passions. I was drawn to the possibility of learning a new language or immersing myself in a new culture. I knew there was more for me to do outside of school. I had an itch to explore the world and broaden my horizons.

CHAPTER 9

GROWTH

I noticed that I was becoming a bit impatient and was looking for a change of environment. I had always dreamed of studying abroad while in college, but I did not think that my dream would be realized since my health was very unstable. Now that I had had a transplant, the world was open to me, and my dreams could be actualized. So one day, I walked into the study abroad office and inquired about my options. I was a senior at this point, and the idea of being a senior in college and spending time with younger students was not very appealing, but I decided to keep an open mind. I had called my friend Theresa to ask for some advice on this matter. I was nervous since I knew my parents would raise health concerns around my travels, so I hoped that she could give me perspective. Theresa is an avid traveler who had visited over thirty countries by the time I met her. She is adventurous, free-spirited, and has no limits. I admired her lifestyle, so she was the perfect person to talk to. She told me that I had to go—that it would be one of the best experiences I ever had because it would open my eyes to the world. In the excitement of it all,

I finished work (I was a tutor for underprivileged kiddos) and then went straight home to share my enthusiasm with my parents; however, I was met with concerns about how I would respond to being away from my family. What if I had a similar response to my time at UCSD and wanted to come back home soon after leaving? They were hesitant, but they also saw the excitement and joy in my eyes, so they gave me permission to apply for the program. The process was tedious, but I was finally approved: destination San Sebastian, Spain! I was told that I would be attending a local university with students from multiple colleges. I was the only one from my university attending, but this would challenge me to open up and develop new friendships. I was thrilled, yet extremely nervous, and at times I second-guessed my decision. Things that are not familiar are always uncomfortable, but I knew that I had to keep pushing the edges of my comfort zone to grow.

I began to prepare for my trip and purchased all of the gear I needed. I was excited to finally have the chance to do something that I had been anticipating for so long. As I said goodbye to my loved ones, I began to feel an overarching sense of sadness. This experience was exciting for me; however, I was worried that I would not have as good of a time without them. I wished that they were coming with me. Before this opportunity, I had not traveled to Europe or many other places. There was a world out there that I did not know much about, but I was thrilled to explore. This was the beginning of my yearning to see the world's beauty and encounter the paths less traveled. I boarded the airplane and off I went.

Once I landed, the tour guide picked me up and brought along a group of students on a bus to Madrid. They wanted us to have the chance to connect with other exchange students so that once we separated, there would be camaraderie among us. We saw so many beautiful sights: the Plaza Mayor, museums, architecture, nightlife, and more! The cuisine was unfamiliar to me, which was a challenge. Spanish people love their pork! The streets were lined with shops selling dried, cured, and fresh pork. Food is an essential aspect of Spanish culture, so I was open-minded to try new things. There was little variety in the type of cuisine; seafood and pork were plentiful. As a flexitarian who leans toward vegetarian, I did not have other options, which forced me to get out of my comfort zone. I was exposed to so much that was different from my California lifestyle, which was an incredible growth opportunity. My hope going into this program was to gain a "typical" college experience of making new friends and not have any concerns apart from school, grades, partying, and connecting. Though the people I was around were almost all a year or two younger than I was, I still learned so much from them. They were all young and carefree, which was something I had not genuinely experienced since my diagnosis at the age of fifteen. There were times when everyone was going out and asked me if I wanted to join, but I would say no. I was still getting comfortable around alcohol and the possible judgment around how people viewed me in a social setting. I was continually battling resistance around these thoughts, and it was a long journey to build my confidence, self-worth, forgiveness, mindfulness, and so much more. I was genuinely appreciative of the special people I met who allowed me to be in my space and grow at my pace. I experienced so many beautiful landmarks, people (souls), and memories during my time there. I had the chance to spend weekends or holidays traveling to Germany, Turkey, France, Portugal, and other cities within Spain. The trip was very beneficial for my growth, since I allowed myself to explore, build courage, gain confidence, learn independence, responsibility, and adventure. As my time drew to a close, I planned to visit family in London and spend Christmas there before returning home. I had spoken to my family back home occasionally during my time in Spain. The prepaid phone was not very reliable, it was costly/confusing to use, and the internet was spotty. When I did get a chance to connect with them, it was nice to hear that everyone was well and learn about what they were up to. It also allowed me to connect with my grandma, who I was very close to (she helped raise my siblings and me). She had lived with us for my entire life and we shared a close bond. During my time abroad, my sisters told me that my grandma was not doing well. She had fallen and was asked by the doctors to rest to ensure her recovery. She had a hip replacement a few years earlier after a bad fall, so I was worried about her. She had always been resilient and seemed to bounce back every time, so I did not think this time would be any different. As the weeks went by, I heard that she was becoming delirious and could not take care of herself, so she required a lot of physical support. The last time I spoke with her, she asked how I was doing; we talked about our health and taking care of ourselves. I did not want her to be worried about me, so I reassured her that I was doing well and looking forward to seeing her. Unfortunately, this was the last time I would ever get to talk to my Ba (grandma). The week before Thanksgiving, I got the call from my family that my Ba was now in the hospital. She was barely speaking, no longer coherent, and declining rapidly. I believe she had a heart attack and her body was beginning to shut down. Come to find out, the last stint she had in the hospital had led to an infection that got so bad that it eventually left her in sepsis. Her body could no longer fight. She was now on a ventilator and her chances of recovery were slim. Hearing all of this from thousands of miles away did not leave me hopeful. I felt very helpless, guilty, and sad. How could this happen? I did not have the time with her that I felt I should have had. I wanted to at least be with her during her final days and take care of her the way she had done for my siblings and me our entire lives. I wanted to show gratitude.

I was torn between following through with my commitment to complete my program or going home to be with my family. My parents had called and said that, as an extended family, they had decided to take her off the ventilator, but they would wait if I wanted to come back home before they "pulled the plug." I could not stay any longer. I had the realization that nothing else mattered at that moment but being with my family. I shared the terrible news with my roommates, teachers, and advisors. They were all very supportive. Within a matter of hours, I had booked the next flight out of Madrid and packed up my belongings. I was sent away with the graceful hugs of my roommates and well-wishes for my travels and family. As I wiped away tears, I began the countdown of my journey back home. As I got closer to home, all I could think of was visiting my Ba. Everyone in my family was taking turns staying with her and spending the night.

My sister met me at the airport. Our greeting was bittersweet because besides my grief over my Ba, I was meeting my niece for the first time. The drive home was sad. I was restless in my desire to see my Ba. I had just landed in California after months in Europe away from my family and was coming home to devastating circumstances. I got home and greeted everyone and then we sat down together for Thanksgiving dinner. As we celebrated a holiday that signifies the importance of gratitude, we took turns sharing the ways in which we were grateful for my Ba and the years we had shared with her. She had influenced us all through years of nurturing and wisdom. She had lived with us for all of our lives, so it was *tough* knowing that she would no longer be with us. As we continued our meal, all I could think about was driving over to see her. I wanted to have some time alone and connect with her in the hope that somehow she could hear me. She was intubated on a ventilator and her body was puffy. She was almost unrecognizable, but her face looked the same. As I entered the room, the silence was cut by the sounds of the machines and all I could do was cry. I wanted to be with her one more time and share everything I had never told her directly. As I whispered words of love, healing, and appreciation in her ear, I felt her presence. The following day would be her last, so I wanted to make this conversation count. I confronted my sadness about her leaving since she belonged with us, at home. I recognized that her soul would always be with us, but her body (the vessel) for her soul had moved on. I know I will always have her with me, in my heart and mind —*always*! The next day, my entire family got together—all of my grandmother's children and grandchildren. As she was being removed from the ventilator, we waited in the family room. One by one we went in to give her our last blessings on her journey to a kinder place. I went in with Hina, trying to hold on and be a pillar of support for my family, but as we walked away from her, I completely broke down. I could no longer keep it in; my body was telling me to grieve. My sister and I held on to each other and comforted one another outside of my grandmother's room. Time ticked on as she took her last breath, and just like that, as her life had come into the world, so it left. For years after my grandmother's death, I struggled with guilt because I had not been with her during the last few months of her life. I had not gotten to share with her all that I wished for her to know. I would lie in bed at night and ask the universe to bring my Ba back to me. I attempted to open a portal in my mind to contact my grandmother one last time. I was on a quest to have her reveal herself to me and would not stop until I saw her for myself as a spirit that had passed on. She was on my mind always. If she was not, then I might lose the memory of her and I could not let that happen. The constant longing for her was not healthy, but I did not know how to shut off that part of my mind. Every time I spoke about her or thought about our time together, I cried. I had not fully dealt with my grief over her loss, so any mention or thought of her could completely break me down. The pain went on for years because I had never dealt with grief to this extent for someone I loved so much, but the lesson I learned from this experience is that trying to guilt or pressure myself over the death of a loved one will not bring me closure. Also, focusing on something so firmly won't get me what I want. The best I could do was process my grief and focus on the shared moments I had with my Ba, so her memory could live on. I was grateful to be home and surrounded by love. Love truly cures and conquers all.

CHAPTER 10

CONNECTION

Coming home so abruptly was a shock, but being with my family and processing my grief with loved ones lifted me. It was now early 2014 and I finally felt more like myself again. Life was looking lighter and more hopeful. One day, while Sona and I were hanging out, she invited me to meet a friend of hers and I agreed. Sona and I arrived at a hookah lounge/restaurant to meet with her friend, who happened to bring a friend along. This sounded suspiciously like a double date, but I was open to going along with it. The evening passed quickly as we connected over food and laughter. While we were eating, I shared with the guys that I had a kidney transplant and could not eat some of the ordered dishes. The small yet significant conversation set the tone for the relationship I built with these guys. I was open and comfortable with putting things about myself on the table because I had nothing to lose. Being honest was not going to hurt me, and at the end of the day, I was looking at them as friends, nothing more. What did I have to prove to them? The evening ended with my dropping off the guys at their home.

One of them caught my attention because he was genuine, humorous, giving, and had an aura about him. I was nervous around him and had butterflies every time I saw him, so I knew that something inside me was telling me to pursue this feeling. We ended up exchanging numbers and within days we went on our first date. I had found someone I truly cared about and was hopeful that this would be a lasting relationship. However, as quickly as sparks flew, my lack of experience, maturity, and knowing what I wanted led to a short-lived relationship. I wanted to be fully invested in this person, but I had childish ways of expressing my desire to further pursue the relationship. I was also playing hard to get and not being clear about what I wanted from a partner. This guy is eight years older than I am, so he was clear about the type of partner he was seeking; however, it was the opposite of who I was. I found myself trying to conform to fit his criteria, which eventually led to miscommunication and a dramatic end to our relationship. I had hoped that we would continue dating, since we had developed a deep connection that I had not experienced before. However, this was not a good reason to continue the relationship. After reflecting on what he was asking of me and looking for in a partner, I realized that we were not meant for each other. The relationship took a toll on my mental health because I had not previously opened myself up to the opposite sex. Now that I had, it was just feeding that story I once believed: "I will never get married because no one in the world would want to be in a relationship and create a family with someone who has a long-term chronic illness." He was a traditional man with deep cultural ties that affected his perception of the world. He wanted a woman to prioritize her family and kids and possibly sacrifice a career to ensure that the family is cared for. Preferably a woman who was a vegetarian, had no tattoos, and wanted to bear his children. I was none of those. How did I expect to be with someone by changing myself, when I was still discovering who I was? When I first was diagnosed, pregnancy had not been a concern since I was so young, but as I got older, I recognized that it was something that I should discuss in order to be empowered and prepared to make such a big decision. Once I received my transplant, I got much more detailed information about the things that I "can" and "cannot" do. Well, these are suggestions based on research and medical opinions. I was told that carrying children would require me to have considerable observation by physicians since the pregnancy would be high risk. They recommended that I consider other options first before risking my life and the baby's life. I had shared this information with the guy I was dating, as it was important to discuss this topic with him. I know it is not easy for many women to discuss fertility. This is an incredibly challenging, but necessary, conversation for women with kidney disease or any other life-threatening condition. I made it clear that I was not willing to risk my life to bear children, as other wonderful options would allow me to be a parent. I was saddened that my body would not permit the miracle of bringing life into this earth. I felt "less than" because my body would have difficulty and potentially kill me if I chose to carry a child. I struggled with worthiness for many years around this topic. Years later, when I spoke with Dr. Hashmi, he encouraged me to consider planning a family. He shared that I should not take any options off the table because I am still young and healthy. I could carry a child to full term with proper care and monitoring by a medical team. It was news that I had not expected ever to hear, but it was encouraging. I was appreciative of shifting away from the limiting conversations of the past and now having an open dialogue about potentially experiencing pregnancy. After that talk, I realized that the possibilities were endless.

Once pregnancy became a focal point of my conversation with the man I was dating at the time, it began to take a toll on me. I was tying the issue of pregnancy to my identity, which grew into disappointment that I could not do something that comes so naturally to many women. Thinking about planning a future family was taxing on my mental health, so I swore off dating. I had made a mistake in allowing myself to care for and possibly consider a future with this man. From that time on, I did not share with most of the guys I dated that I have CKD. I did not want them to define me by it and not consider dating me because of it. I tried to hide who I was because I could not handle another rejection. I placed a shield around my heart. I can now say that I was inauthentic by removing the vulnerability of sharing a huge part of my life.

Although I wanted to be the ideal person for someone to date, I shifted my focus, and the priority of my life became to finish school and hustle. At this point, the guy and I had moved past our differences and decided to be friends. I should have known that this was not a good idea. Being friends with him was a mistake because he continued to have access to my life without healthy boundaries in place. After reflecting on how things ended, I still had a "back door," thinking that if we were still friends, then maybe there was a chance we would date again with a better outcome. It was hard to maintain a friendship with him and not have that "what if" thought in the back of my mind. I found reasons to connect with him whenever I could, and this went on for two years—way longer than it should have! Eventually, I got to the place mentally where I asked myself, "What do I have to lose?" I was stuck on this person not because of what there was between us, but because of what there was not. My ego was bruised and it wanted to redeem itself by getting the guy in the end. Clearly, this was not the right intention to lead with, but I was confident in myself and finally built up the courage to go after what I wanted. One day as I sat at work, I was flooded with uneasiness. My mind kept racing as I pondered reaching out to him to make plans. As the hours passed and the back and forth continued, I grabbed my phone and sent him a message asking to meet up. I was sweating profusely, palms sweaty and heart racing, as I anxiously awaited his response. Keep in mind that I had not seen him in almost two years, but if I did not take the chance now, then when would I? I did not want to have any regrets. Luckily, he replied and we set up a time to meet. As I prepared to meet him, my focus turned to dressing up and looking fabulous, so he would be reminded of what he could still have. (These are things that girls do, and I am a girl.) As we sat and spoke, I took the lead in sharing the feelings I still had for him and asking if he had any interest in pursuing dating again. He said he was interested, so I asked if the things that had bothered him in the past (vegetarianism, biological kids, etc.) were still factors that would affect whether we moved forward or not. He still held firm on some of those things. He was open to seeing where the relationship went, but that would mean I would have to think long and hard about committing. I said I would think about it, and then we could talk and plan our next hangout. As time went on, he did not engage much or initiate. I was growing frustrated because I expected in my mind that things would be different and they were not going as I had hoped. As the weeks went by, I grew angry and disappointed, so I shared with him that I did not feel he cared about our friendship or me. Our discussion led nowhere, so we eventually met once more to talk. I went into the conversation confident, being true to myself, and asking for what I wanted. Ultimately, it ended with the answer I was looking for: this relationship would not continue. We were not meant for each other and that is okay. I could now close this chapter in my life and move forward. Meeting him and going through that roller coaster of emotions encouraged me not to settle. I had an epiphany in the summer of 2016, before trying to reconcile with him, and it was this: I want to get married and have a family with someone who wants me as their equal, accepts me for who I am, and supports me in my endeavors. I was going to get what I deserved, and nothing would stop me. I was on a mission!

In early 2017, I had just come back from India after visiting family and attending my cousin's wedding. Being around a few weddings and being asked about when I was going to get married led me to eventually get on a dating app. It was something that I had tried to hold off on, in the hope of finding my soulmate in person at a coffee shop; however, I did not have high hopes of finding someone in person, so I decided to diversify my options and access more people by joining a dating app. I was super-anxious and could not bear to engage on the app myself, so with the help of my best friend, Manpreet, we created an account. She was given the title of matchmaker, so I could avoid having to do the legwork. The app was short-lived, but I met a few men I attempted to pursue during the few weeks that I had a profile. Dating was now at the forefront of my mind. I believe everyone experiences this short period of heightened focus on dating at some point in their lives. Eventually, you calm down and find dating a lighthearted, enjoyable experience, instead of thinking that "*I have to get married*" and the next person I go out with could be *"the one."* This sounds very dramatic, and it is; however, it is usually only a phase. When I was in this phase, I would find myself in different parts of town several evenings a week for a first or second date. I was not desperate, but I felt that being out there and engaged with people would boost my chances of finding a compatible partner. Going on dates had its pros and cons. The pros were that I got to have new experiences by meeting new people and going to new places; the cons were that some dates were awkward or uncomfortable. Dating has a spectrum of emotions and experience levels, but it is rewarding in the end as long as you remain present to your intention and goal. The intention can vary—it doesn't have to mean a serious relationship— but it's essential to be clear about what you're looking for to find the type of relationship you want, whether casual, serious, or anywhere else on the spectrum. I found that writing down what I desired in a partner helped me weed out men that did not capture my interest. It was with this specific list that I manifested Shiv (my fiancé). I wrote a very detailed list because it gave me clarity on my non-negotiables and the things I was willing to compromise on. Once I identified these points, I knew what questions to ask while on dates. I discussed important questions early on to avoid wasting time and misleading a person. This approach gave me the boost of morale I needed to navigate dating. I realized that it is okay to have standards that I won't budge on. I was not going to settle for anything less.

Getting clear on what I was looking for took me a while because I first wanted to gain clarity on myself. Who was I? I needed to get to know myself on a deeper, more intimate level and reach a place of being happy with myself. It was not that I did not want to be in a healthy, loving relationship—far from it. I recognized that I wanted to expand my perspective to gain insight into myself so that when I eventually did meet the "right person," he would be someone that I could receive openly. I wanted to learn to challenge and depend on myself, so I figured I should go beyond studying abroad and attempt to travel solo. I had never done this before, but I was ready for an adventure. Graduation was around the corner, and I had no plans to apply for a job, at least not yet, because I was working with my parents, which allowed me to create a flexible schedule for myself. I figured traveling would be a gift to myself to enjoy life and allow myself to indulge after all of the hard work I had put into completing my degree. As I looked into where I wanted to go, something about Bali, Indonesia seemed to resonate. I had watched *Eat, Pray, Love*, and maybe the Julia Roberts in me was thinking, "Let's go on a journey of self-actualization." So I did. After some online research, I decided to start the trip by volunteering to teach English while exploring the island of Bali. The teaching gig would only be for three weeks, so I figured I could expand on that and create a two-month-long Asia adventure. I had always wanted to visit Cambodia because of Angkor Wat, so I began to build my itinerary, which eventually came to include Bali, Cambodia, Thailand, Hong Kong, and China. My sister ended up joining in Thailand and her being there made the experience feel like home.

As I landed in Bali, I was amazed at the gorgeous beaches, greenery, and culture. I connected with some delightful ladies whom I still consider to be friends to this day. We would go out dancing in the evenings or ride scooters through the city with our French crew (a group of French guys who were lovely). We enjoyed fireside dinners on the beach, yoga in the middle of a forest, and delicious organic food just a short walk away. I would spend hours (and I do mean hours) at two specific cafes, Kopi Desa and Vespa Cafe, just pondering life and enjoying good conversations with friends. Those places left such a deep warmth in my heart that to this day I can feel the peace and joy I experienced there by imagining myself walking up to the coffee shop. As I approach the counter at Kopi Desa, I recognize the faces of people I have met. I order coffee (usually a mocha latte) and then take a seat on one of the chairs near the outside steps. The sunlight beams down on me while I have my coffee and enjoy laughs with friends. I feel at home: comfortable, secure, and free. I take off my shoes and fold my legs into a lotus position while observing others (mainly foreigners) relaxing. It is my home away from home.

I felt spoiled, honestly, because Bali was much more than I had ever imagined. The kiddos I taught brought me the most joy because they were curious, inviting, and fun. They were kindergartners with attention spans of only ten to fifteen minutes, so the class was taken lightly. A European girl and I were assigned to this classroom to teach English a few times a week and I was prepared. I had taught English before for a group of elementary students while in Spain, so I had some familiarity with the school environment. It was always rewarding to work with children since their brains are like sponges and absorb so much information. I found myself bringing my walls down and stretching mentally. I learned new things and relied on myself to make decisions that caused me to trust myself and follow my intuition. Without my family and friends, I learned to be vulnerable by letting my guard down emotionally and trusting others. I was free, unfiltered, and myself. I did not want to leave, but knew that the beautiful memories and new friends would be a great start to the rest of my trip. I next went to Siem Reap, Cambodia, and spent an entire week by myself exploring the city. I was unsure of what to expect, but I created a plan and allowed the rest of my trip to play out. I was anxious and slightly fearful of the unknown. I had lovely hostel hosts, who made me feel more at home. I purchased some adventure packages, including an ATV ride through the Cambodian countryside and lunch cooked by locals. I also hired a tuk-tuk (a motorized open taxi that reminds me of India). The driver was my guide for three days, picking me up in the morning and dropping me off in the evening after a long day of exploring the many temples in this mysterious, ancient city. I was amazed at the calm, peaceful, and beautiful presence of Angkor Wat, even with thousands of people walking its grounds every day. My guide was kind, knowledgeable, and helpful. He took me across the countryside, close to the Laos border, to enjoy an old park with a scenic waterfall. I can say that it was one of the most exciting rides of my life—the wind in my hair, the silence of the drive cut by the sound of the motor, and the natural, untouched environment far away from the hustle and bustle of the city. I basked in gratitude for being healthy and having the freedom to live such a life. People cannot often pick up and leave for months to travel and explore the world. Leaving Cambodia was bittersweet because I loved the city and wanted to continue exploring; however, I was limited in some of my explorations because I was alone, which made me feel a bit uncomfortable.

As my trip progressed, the time spent learning about other cultures and having new awareness influenced my perspective. My time in Thailand was lively; the people are jovial and the culture is enchanting. I spent my days on the dreamy beaches with clear, blue water. My nights were spent wandering the busy streets bustling with night markets, Muay Thai shows, and ping-pong bars. This was a stark contrast to my time in Hong Kong, which was primarily spent at customs trying to retrieve my medication in their custody. I do not want to paint a bad picture of the region; however, with that incident I recognized that many people like myself experience prejudice. The government questioned me about whether or not I was a drug dealer importing pills to sell in their land (in their words). They took my passport and stated that I was bringing in illegal drugs. I was there to pick up a kidney medication that I had lost while in Thailand. My mom had shipped it to me to avoid having to abruptly end my trip without visiting Beijing. I was treated like a criminal. After two days of inquiry, I was finally allowed to have my medication, thanks to the note of a well-informed doctor at the airport (who told me that what they were doing was illegal) stating that the medication was essential for my kidney transplant. I did not report the injustice, but I should have. I left the city with a warning placed on my record, so now I am mindful of always taking a medical note during my travels. This unwarranted setback left me hoping for a better experience on the last leg of my trip—mainland China. It was at the top of my list of places to visit, and being a cultural buff, I wanted to see the Great Wall. I was so close that I figured, "Why not go for a week and then cross that off my bucket list?" I was not at all prepared for this leg of the trip, mentally or physically. I went from very sunny, tropical weather to a frigid environment. I had purchased a few items while in Hong Kong, including a pair of boots and a coat that I literally wore every day. I had one small suitcase at this point with very minimal items so that I could move around freely between cities and hostels. This part of my trip was the most difficult. I was not expecting to feel so completely out of place and like a total foreigner. I know, I know—I was in another country, so technically I was a foreigner; however, I was made to feel uncomfortable by the majority of the population because I was one of the very few brown people in the country. I did not speak a word of Mandarin, and everyone around me either did not speak English or was unwilling to help. One of my goals for the trip was to challenge my identity and learn to be independent and self-reliant. I have since learned that this is part of my personality—wanting to have control because of trust issues, which makes it difficult for me to depend on others. This sounds like a radical experiment of challenging myself in another country, but I knew it would either make or break me. There was a point during my trip at which I wanted to give in, give up, and go home; however, I was unwilling to accept defeat. I refocused on my goal and intention of visiting China and pushed forward. I arrived in China, and the first thing I noticed was the cold breeze and sparse airport. I was eager to get out and see things, but soon came across my first hurdle—getting on the train. I went up to the ticket booth to purchase a ticket, but the attendant did not speak English. How was I going to buy a ticket? I was tensing up, afraid of being stranded. I handed her some money and hoped that it was enough to buy me a one-way ticket to the city. I scurried across the platform to reach the train before it left, pushing past the rail, when the cops yelled. They were shouting at the top of their lungs because I was not following the proper protocol. I had to go back in line and pass security. There was an extensive line of people and I suddenly heard a woman speak up and say, "Follow me. I can help you." She was a middle-aged woman who had lived in the States for many years and was now visiting family. I jumped at the opportunity and followed her. She was a very sweet, caring, and giving woman. I shared with her where I was going—a hostel in the heart of Beijing. As she gave me directions, I quickly jotted down notes on a piece of paper. Hopefully, they were legible because it was time for her to get on another train. I had just met her and then she was gone. Now I would be back to venturing off on my own, hoping that my journey would get easier. I got off at the Tiananmen Square exit and emerged into a cold, dark night. I walked around the station to see if I could find someone else to ask for directions, but there was no one. Neither could I find a taxi to hop into and ask to drop me off at my hostel. This was concerning, but I decided to choose a direction and start walking. As I walked down the steps to an underground street crossing, I came across a young woman. I approached her; my voice was almost frantic. She stopped while I asked her if she could direct me to my hostel. Luckily, she spoke English! She did not hesitate to offer to walk me to the hostel. I was in *shock*! I couldn't believe the friendly gesture. She told me she did not want to see a woman walking alone late at night. We struck up a conversation during our walk, and she asked what my plans were while visiting the country. I said, "I mainly came to see the Great Wall. Other than that, I have no plans." She asked if I was interested in joining her the following day for a tour of Tiananmen Square with one of her friends. I jumped at the opportunity and said I would see her tomorrow. Suddenly I paused and said, "Wait, how am I going to contact you? Can I add you on Facebook?" She chuckled at my question as I realized that social media is banned in China. She reassured me that I would not have to worry; she would be at my hostel at 8 a.m. sharp. I felt some relief at finally reaching my hostel and was ready to call it a night. I was lucky to get some internet connection through a VPN and message my sister. At this point, I was pondering whether or not I should get the next flight back home. Maybe

I was not ready for this trip? My sister went into support mode and calmed my nerves, reassuring me that she and my family would support whatever decision I made. She was ready to book me a ticket if I asked, which was exactly what I needed to hear. I have always had the support of my family, anywhere and anytime. I am immensely grateful for their vital support, which has given me confidence over the years to take risks and explore new opportunities. I have a judgment-free support system that I can always fall back on, knowing that they will catch me without hesitation. The next morning, I woke up anxious to be ready on time and not miss our meeting. I hoped that the day would be exciting enough to move me past the doubt I had dealt with the night before. As I walked toward the front desk, there she was. Ahh . . . relief! As we stepped out onto the city streets, it felt like the spotlight was turned on me. I stuck out like a sore thumb. Here I was, a brown girl walking alongside my local friend and her Nigerian friend who was there for his studies. The stares were nonstop. The unwarranted comments were obvious, but we did not allow them to hinder our tour of the city. Ultimately, I made a loving, kind-hearted friend, which made my trip worthwhile. She showed me around the city and took the time to make my trip as exciting and adventurous as possible. She was a godsend. The Great Wall, which was the reason I was there, was vast and beautiful—a sight to be seen. Next, it was time to go to Shanghai and visit a friend of mine from UCSD. I enjoyed time with her and her friends. I also had some downtime, which was a striking difference from my visit to Beijing. Although I was enjoying my travels, the anticipation of going home began to overtake my emotions. I realized that opening up and being vulnerable had allowed me to meet beautiful people who supported me throughout the trip. I also recognized a deep love and gratitude for my family, who are always there with a helping hand whenever I need them. They can anticipate my needs before I face them, which shows how deeply we are connected. I am genuinely appreciative of the family and friends that I have.

CHAPTER 11

DECISIONS

Home sweet home. I was happy to be back with my family after a tough leg of my trip. I had relied on them tremendously during my time in Beijing and I was grateful for that support system. As things began to settle, I got back into the routine of work and expanded my responsibilities. I had graduated in the summer with a degree in anthropology and a minor in finance. I was not sure how my degree would be of use because I was focused on expanding my family's business. My parents had always shared with my siblings and me that family was important, and we would continue our business for generations to come. It was my duty to give my time and energy to a career in the hospitality industry. The future looked promising. I was excited about the opportunity to help my parents prosper an already established business. I had worked for them for about eight years by the time I graduated from college. I appreciated the flexibility it provided me, so I could travel and participate in other activities. I had placed a lot of importance on flexibility because I enjoyed my freedom. As time went on, I began to feel unsettled and asked my parents for more responsibility. I realized later (through therapy) that I was trying to prove my capabilities. I had graduated from college and had worked for my parents for many years, so I was expecting them to acknowledge my hard work and recognize my value to the business. Around this time, my brother had just graduated from college in hospitality and now wanted to be part of the family business. He had always been distant from the business in the past, so it was surprising to hear about his change of heart. My parents were excited and jumped at the opportunity because their one and only son now wanted to control the family legacy. To me, it seemed unfair. I had been helping them for so long that I figured they would value me when the time came to transfer responsibility for the business. At the time, I managed four out of the six properties, and I was unsure what role my brother would have or if he would take over some of my duties. Would he just come right in and take charge? I was getting more and more uncomfortable with the idea of sharing responsibility, and my fear and anxiety began to take over my thoughts. This was a very dark and tumultuous time for me, with a lot of anger and frustration leading my thoughts, actions, and feelings. I was not happy with how I showed up, but I believed there was blatant injustice and I chose to stand up for myself. One day, I sat down with my parents and told them that what was happening was unfair. Why were they paying my brother more than me when I had worked for them for ten years trying to prove my worth? I recognized later that this breakdown was more of a worthiness conversation about myself than a conversation about my brother. My brother and I had been very close when we were younger. We were only two years apart in age, so we spent a lot of time playing sports together or getting into trouble. It had been like that until I was diagnosed, after which I had to adjust to an entirely new lifestyle. As the years went on, we became more and more distant. We each had our own growing to do, and once he returned home from college, tensions were high between us. One day I was crying while speaking with my parents because I was frustrated. How could they not see that I was hurt? As our conversation continued, I observed that my point was not being heard, and they suggested that I go out and get another job. I had listened to my parents make this comment before but immediately take it back once they realized that another job would affect the work I did for their business. It is hard to give your energy to multiple things without losing effectiveness, so I had not considered additional work—until now. They challenged me at that moment to expand my responsibilities, so I began to think. The conversation ended with my parents letting me know that they would give me one property to lease and suggesting that the change in responsibilities would allow me to have time for a "9 to 5 job." I had multiple breakdowns leading up to that point and many conversations with trusted people where I said, "I am done. I cannot work for my parents anymore. I should find another job to have a more "peaceful life." I remember one moment very well, which was right before I went to my first EDC (Electric Daisy Carnival) festival with my best friend and I cried the entire morning. She saw that I was distressed and calmed me down by reassuring me about my feelings while creating space for me to vent. I was frustrated about being in a toxic, unhealthy work environment with my parents. I questioned whether I should go because I felt guilty about leaving. We had just argued, and my leaving could be a reason for my parents to say that I was irresponsible. I felt like I owed them my entire time and attention since they were my bosses. I recognized later that I did not feel like my parents' child, but more of a personal assistant or employee, which should have been a red flag. It was not their fault; it was the fact that we had not created healthy boundaries to separate work from personal life. After this realization, I accepted my brother's role in the business. I stepped into a place of trusting him as he took ownership and accepted the majority of the business's responsibilities. There was a positive shift between us as we realized that the argument I had with my parents was not worth losing our relationship over. I wanted the best for him and saw that I was trying to have control over the situation versus taking a step back and allowing him to gain experience. Once I trusted him, my relationship with him changed for the better. The shift happened right before I decided that I would move on from having a significant role in the family business to pursuing my passions.

I have had many jobs in the past, as well as internships and volunteer positions because I am interested in many different things. I volunteered for Habitat for Humanity, an animal shelter, the YMCA, and several other places. I enjoyed giving my time to charities and nonprofits because it always brought me joy to give back to my community by supporting and empowering others. One of my favorite opportunities was being a camp counselor for a group of young kidney patients, a collaboration between the YMCA and the Kidneys Quest Foundation. This experience was the first time I had encountered a group of young kidney patients. I knew this camp would help give them some normalcy and help them build relationships with other patients their age. The lesson I drew from this experience was to find opportunities to give back, especially for people with our unique challenges, because we can give others hope and support by sharing our stories.

The more we share and connect, the more lives we can impact. Each one of us matters.

Aside from volunteering, I enjoyed several different professions during my search to find my purpose. I joined an eco-fashion company as an intern, which was exciting. I have always loved fashion because it is a means of expressing oneself. I had a dream of starting a denim line because although I loved jeans, it was hard to find jeans that fit my tall, thin frame. This introduction to fashion was eye-opening and much more difficult than I had imagined. It is good to shoot for the stars and dream big, but it's also essential to gain some exposure to what you want to do before fully committing to it. After my internship, I moved on to tutoring youth, selling real estate, hand modeling, and merchandising for a jewelry association. When I leased my parents' business, I recognized that real estate was not exactly what I wanted to do. I was more interested in significant investment and commercial deals, but what I was doing was far from that. I recognized that I did not want to be a salesperson who knocked on doors for something I was unsure of and not passionate about. I was still dedicated to getting another job, so I applied for a few jobs each day and waited to hear from an employer. I submitted applications for a variety of jobs in an attempt to find a position that I was passionate about. I got hired by a jewelry merchandising company, which was exciting, flexible, and creative. I saw potential in the company and the job helped me recognize that I could push myself beyond what I thought I was capable of. After some reflection, I realized that I was living an unhealthy lifestyle: spending four hours commuting, three days a week, while leasing a business and managing operations. I was rushing from place to place with hardly any time for myself. It was almost as if I avoided being with myself, as I became engulfed by my tasks while remaining on autopilot, merely moving from one thing to the next.

The job, however, was a great experience that taught me many important lessons and gave me a new perspective on what I wanted for myself. I learned very quickly and became a vital person in the office. I grew close to my colleagues and recognized the potential of working there; however, I knew it would not last for more than a few years. I was growing frustrated with the routine and mundane tasks, and I wanted more. I knew I had much more potential, so I started thinking about what I could do to realize it. My boss began asking me to commit full time, so I shared my truth with her. At her suggestion, I created a formal letter with my requests. I knew the company would agree with my proposal, but deep down inside, I also knew that a promotion would not solve my restlessness. A different title or more pay would not help. I required a profound rewiring. I wrote the letter but chose not to submit it because I knew I did not want the higher position, so it would be unfair to take the opportunity away from someone who authentically wanted it. I would essentially be robbing the company of a dedicated, passionate employee if I chose to stay. So before heading home one night, I went into my boss's office and shared that I would be stepping down from my job; however, I would give her a month's notice to onboard a new hire. This decision was not personal, but a culmination of fatigue, confusion, dissatisfaction, and a desire for change. During this time, I was also handling some health setbacks that affected my kidney transplant, so I recognized that I needed to prioritize my health. I had been battling an infection, which required a few days of hospitalization. My kidney function had decreased drastically. This was especially alarming because I did not have any symptoms of infection. I was left in complete *shock*! Luckily, I avoided sepsis. I would be given multiple rounds of antibiotics to regain my health in the months ahead. I had stopped paying attention to my health, and this was my wake-up call. I was nervous about speaking with my boss about my recent hospitalization because she was unaware of my kidney condition. I had not shared it with her due to the fear of judgment and the possibility of not being hired. With this in mind, I was hesitant to approach her and share my concerns, but my health was declining. So I went into her office one day, and we had an honest, transparent conversation about where I was mentally and physically. I could no longer run on fumes or I would burn myself to the ground. She understood and was saddened to see me leave. At that moment, I felt empowered. I had chosen to speak my truth and take action on something important to me—my health. I have learned from experience that it is imperative to be mindful of your health, especially if you have a health condition. Work stress can harm your health, so it is essential to choose a career you are passionate about or one that prioritizes your health to avoid causing additional stress in your life.

PART III

HEALING

CHAPTER 12

FORGIVENESS

As I reached these conclusions and began to process my dissatisfaction with work, I started to take action. I decided to change my circumstances, so I could live a fuller, more joyful life. I began seeing a therapist again and made progress, but there was a hill in front of me that I couldn't get past. I don't mean a literal hill, but something was holding me back figuratively, and I thought that if I could overcome it, I wouldn't have any woes. I assumed that once I climbed that hill, my growth would peak, and there would be nothing left to overcome as I worked to accomplish my goals. Boy oh boy, was I wrong! I was thinking in limited terms, and I know now there is no such thing as peaking in personal development. Well, I was on a mission to peak mentally, so one day, when Hina mentioned a program she was going to attend in San Diego, I asked questions and picked her brain about it. She spoke of the program enthusiastically, telling me that it was an emotional intelligence leadership academy that focused on supporting people in overcoming obstacles in their lives to live from a place of abundance. I was intrigued, so I continued to ask questions and follow up with her as her program progressed. Each time Hina would come back from a training weekend, I would see lighter energy from her. She would be smiling from ear to ear and speaking into possibilities, which was unlike her. As she began to open up and become vulnerable, I noticed a different side to her. The difference in her was drastic but in a healthy way, which led me to ask her about the possibility of my enrolling in the program. Hina assumed I was not ready for the experience and thought it would better serve me later on after a few more breakdowns and breakthroughs. I was a bit taken aback by her response, but she still hesitated to offer her approval. As I began to challenge her views, she saw that I was committed to growth and open to new possibilities. After a few more conversations with Hina, I decided to enroll. I was now a part of Ascension Leadership Academy, cohort SD 18. The year was 2018—my most life-changing year to date. I was very anxious about the leadership program because I knew that I would only get out of it what I put into it. It was not going to be easy by any means, but I believed that if I trusted the process, then it would ultimately alter my life in a positive direction. I was asked on a screening call what I intended to gain from attending the training. I answered that I wanted to overcome any limiting beliefs I had for myself and let go of past traumas. I no longer wanted to live in a victim mindset. Instead, I was ready to take charge of my life. First, I had to learn to let my walls down by trusting myself and others through vulnerability. I needed to shed the tough persona I had embodied for many years and start sharing parts of my life that were painful, parts that I was scared to share because of the fear that people might judge me. I had told myself that having a tough persona was confidence; however, it was complete insecurity. I did not want to be taken advantage of by men or by people in general by being vulnerable and allowing people into my heart, so I led from a distrusting place. I later learned that vulnerability is power. If you allow your walls to come down and connect from your heart, people will trust you. It's important to find even one person you can trust and begin sharing yourself with to get comfortable with being vulnerable.

It is uncomfortable, especially in the beginning, because you may fear that people will judge you or take advantage of your vulnerability. One person opening up and being vulnerable, however, will lead to others around them doing the same. During my time in the program, I learned to truly let go of the stories I had once used to justify my feelings and actions. I was practically holding myself hostage by continuing to exhibit the same patterns throughout my life. I learned to love myself and allow people to see me for who I truly am. I was no longer holding on to my past, but forging a new, clear picture of myself. There were many tears shed from the pain I had endured throughout my life: being molested, my diagnosis, judgment from others, and the loss of my grandmother. I learned to free myself from the pain, guilt, and anger I had held on to so tightly through forgiveness. Forgiveness for oneself is vital in healing because we harbor guilt, shame, and other emotions that affect our well-being. If I continue to nurse ill feelings, then I won't create the space for love and healing to come into my life. I was ready to let go of the emotions that no longer served me and focus on a healthy mindset by rewiring the way my mind processed thoughts. The activities gave me the closure I had sought for many years. In one activity, my grandmother (Ba) came to me in a vision. She came to be there in an ethereal manner, so graceful and calm. The brief moment of feeling her presence allowed me to relax and finally let go of the many years of guilt I had borne for not being there for her during her last moments. As I embraced her presence, she presented the word "peace" to me. I immediately felt the peace take over my body because I had waited for years to get a sign from my Ba to know that she was not upset with me. Instead, she wanted to relieve me of any stress or sadness I held onto over her passing. She was the only person that could give me peace of mind, and connecting with her gave me the confirmation I needed to let go of guilt and move on. I now had the ultimate peace within myself to release the years of pain and judgment I had endured from others and caused for myself. Now I understood how to lead with peace by removing the judgment toward myself. I had already decided to use my grandmother's eye in a tattoo design, which I had created months prior. This was my way of remembering her and always keeping her close to me. Ironically, my tattoo appointment was set for a few days after she had appeared to me in the activity, so everything came full circle. The universe was conspiring, and now I finally had peace.

The variety of activities facilitated different experiences and outcomes for me. One of the most powerful activities was screaming—loudly and for a lengthy amount of time. As I screamed, the pain in my body dissolved with each breath I took. The repeated screaming purged my body of the many years of unwarranted emotions I held onto. The pain was no longer a part of my being. I prevailed, and now I could experience forgiveness. The journey of forgiveness is not strictly focused on the other person or people you want to forgive, as I had always imagined it to be. I was angry, and my ego would not allow me to forgive others for the pain they had caused me. This allowed me to control and harbor ill feelings, which take a toll on the body. I learned from many in-depth conversations with loved ones that forgiveness is about permitting yourself to let go. I noticed a pattern of not wanting to release control and show grace because it seemed like this would excuse the pain caused by others. I had the opportunity to remove the unhealthy energy by focusing on myself, how I would benefit from moving forward by forgiving the person who caused the pain. This empowering move meant that the other person no longer had a hold on my life. They would no longer have power over me. I was now taking my power back by showing grace to everyone who had caused me pain because I no longer wanted to be a hurt person, who was hurting others. Only when I recognized how much pain I had been keeping inside did I become aware of how deeply affected I was. Another powerful moment was when I finally stood up and spoke, which was very difficult for me. I tend to stay away from the spotlight, but this was my opportunity to stand up for myself and for my life, saying that I mattered, and no one else could decide whether I was worthy of being here. This time, I put myself before others. This was not selfish. I learned that to support others, I must take care of myself first. If I try to give from an "empty cup," then I will be left with no energy for myself. Also, the energy thus given away is lifeless, which doesn't serve anyone. Instead, suppose I come from a "full cup," one filled with self-love, compassion, kindness, patience, and mindfulness. In that case, any person receiving energy from the overflow of love and joy will benefit immensely. The good, healthy energy will go much further than fragmented energy. I recognized that I was giving my energy away to quite a few people that drained me. In college, I focused on participating in more social circles and building many different friendships to relive some of the high school and early college years that I had not experienced like my peers. It was easier for me to step into a place of extroversion and rebuild my social life since I had abandoned my social life after being diagnosed in high school. I wanted to fit in and belong, so I made choices aligned with that because that was my intention during those years. This was when I first tried weed and had alcohol occasionally. The choices I made were in the moment, and although some people may not agree, I have no regrets. I had discussed the repercussions of drinking and smoking with my physicians since it is vital to be informed of the risks. We had in-depth conversations, and albeit they did not entirely agree with me, I understood that it was their responsibility to look out for my best interests. I do occasionally drink. At times I feel as though I am sabotaging my health after being given a second chance by someone else. It is tough to handle, but I know that I am responsible for my actions and recognize that I am human, so things are not always perfect.

As I began to reflect on my behavior, I recognized that I did not feel in alignment with constant socializing, and over time I was being drawn to more subtle forms of socializing. Before I went to ALA, my social life had calmed down quite a bit—just a few hours every other week to meet with friends. It was a stark difference compared to how I had been. I was a person who showed up to anything and everything that I was invited to. Whether I had known you for a day or twenty years, I showed up. Now that I had shifted, I began to make choices that reflected my interests, whether they were popular choices or not. It did leave me saying, "Hey, I have to pass on tonight" many times, but I was content. I realized that saying no or not today was okay. It felt uncomfortable in the beginning, but overall my energy and happiness levels were much higher. In doing this, I was required to recognize the importance of setting boundaries and trusting myself. I lost some friends and acquaintances, but I have no regrets. As I get older, I recognize the things I value, so it is crucial for me to have relationships with people who share the same values and morals. At that time, I was outgrowing certain relationships and realized that I was surrounded by many people who did not challenge me enough in my ways of thinking or give me room to grow. Instead of simply remaining comfortable, I wanted to get the most out of life by seeking challenges to grow and break through limiting beliefs; for example, I was an avid runner in middle school as a member of Students Run LA. The activity was something that I was not entirely passionate about; however, it was something that I enjoyed with friends and gave me the opportunity for new adventures. Once I was diagnosed, I stopped running because I was dealing with fatigue. It was not until ten years later that I picked up running again. I saw it as a challenge, so I signed up for a half marathon. It was something I discussed with my nephrologist, who voiced his concerns about dehydration. However, I continued my training and have now completed two half marathons and multiple 10 to 13 milers. My first half marathon was the Diva's Half Marathon in San Francisco. I ended up getting diagnosed with plantar fasciitis three weeks before the run. I had no choice but to stop running to allow myself to heal; however, the setback did not stop me from completing the run. The feeling afterward of accomplishment and testing my limits led me to almost immediately sign up for the Zion Half Marathon in Utah. At this point, my best friend (Manpreet) and I wanted to continue running together, and I encouraged one of my other friends (Grace) to join us. We all ended up camping in Utah for four nights and had the opportunity to compete in the race together and create new memories with each other. I can say that running brings people together; I have experienced this firsthand. I would encourage others to find a passion to incorporate others into or meet other like-minded people through. There are so many wonderful memories that can be created and shared with others through curiosity and passion. The main thing is to have an open mind and challenge ourselves and what others say about us. We are capable of much more than we think. It is essential to speak up and share what we are hoping to accomplish, so whether others support us or not, we are informed and can make the best decisions. Don't just settle for what other people have to say and not challenge those beliefs. It is imperative to incorporate sustainable growth into our lives, so we do not forgo our full potential. Growth provides us with hope and excitement to work toward a brighter, happier future.

CHAPTER 13

LOVE

I had perceived myself as growing for many years, but there was still a threshold that I had not reached. I recognized that from the time I took on leasing my parents' business until I began ALA, there were substantial mental blocks I was unable to remove. I was very fixated on this energy, which left me stuck. It was all in my mind, but I did not have enough people in my circle to facilitate the process of overcoming these obstacles. ALA was the beginning of discovering my authentic self and learning to say what I want without hesitation. I had been in a victim mindset in many ways because of my past traumas. I had to learn to let those stories go. I created a new story for myself: I am a powerful, loving, and passionate leader. I have all that I want in me. It just hadn't been fully cultivated because I was getting in my own way. I am very prone to self-sabotage, and I allowed what others thought of me to motivate my decisions. I became aware that I had not solidified my belief system. It was very open and susceptible to others' beliefs, so I had to learn to lead with my motivations, which are genuine to me and not influenced by anyone else. My beliefs led me to speak with intention, confidence, and worth. I matter, and I own my voice. This shift was just the beginning of what I now call healing. I appeared much lighter. Things were no longer as devastating to me because I now had the tools to process my emotions, which shifted my perspective and allowed me to create a new narrative for myself. Before this, I had said that I wanted to get married and have a family, but my marriage would be an equal and mutually supportive one. I was afraid that I could not have a partner who would support my endeavors and ambitions without feeling challenged by my presence—one who would be by my side to manage my health without any hesitation. I finally broke through my limiting beliefs, and my wish came to fruition when I met Shiv. We met in ALA, which was something I had not expected. During the program, everyone experiences vulnerability by sharing deep emotions and stories. After one of our tough days, Shiv and I finally connected and hugged each other. It was the first hug of many, but he said that this one broke down his walls and freed the chains around his heart. He had made a point of our connecting after that activity because he was proud of me for speaking up and using my voice to share my story. He had not known anything about me before that, but that moment was powerful and left an impression. I had heard about Shiv through Hina. She was in the program with his best friend, and now they had signed up Shiv and I (separately) for the same cohort. To make a long story short, she had sent me an article about him while I was in Chicago for St. Patty's weekend (the same week I signed up for ALA). She said that she wanted me to meet him, and hopefully I would because he had just signed up to attend the program at the same time. This seemed a bit obvious on her end, but I read the article and was immediately moved. I say this because Shiv is a powerful human being in terms of his passion and interest in impacting the world. I learned of his company, NeuraLace Medical, which created Axon Therapy, a noninvasive technology that provides long-lasting treatment for neuropathic pain. This is a big issue he is tackling, and I was inspired. I said to myself at that moment, "I am going to either marry or be best friends with him." (I ended up choosing both —we are engaged.) Either way, I knew that I wanted him in my life. Keep in mind that this was in March, and the program did not start until the end of June, so I had months to wait. When the first day finally arrived, I was a bit nervous about meeting him since I had some background. I sat in the back to disguise myself, so I could avoid speaking up. At one point, he rose to share who he was. I was now seeing him in person, but I did my best to avoid him the entire first week. It's funny that I said I wanted to connect with him and then did the opposite by avoiding him. Somehow, at the end of the day, we would end up at valet together and have an awkward conversation like, "Hey, that was an intense day, right?" "See you tomorrow." The first weekend passed, and now I only had one week left to make my move. I had not been focused on creating new friendships or getting into a relationship while attending the program. I was strictly there to "get past my shit" so that I could live a freer life. I wanted to launch my platform, Antidote (http://antidotehealth.io), which offers community and encouragement to patients living with kidney disease. I recognized that many fears were holding me back from taking the step of launching. I was hoping that ALA would give me the tools and confidence to launch Antidote successfully, but I gained so much more. The second weekend was when Shiv and I connected on a profound level, and by the end of the second night, he invited me to come over to his place for breathing. I was thinking, "What the heck is 'breathing'? We breathe all day, every day." I was not sure what the activity would entail, but I told him I would consider it. Also, he wanted to breathe around 10 a.m., which at the time was way too early for me. I enjoy waking up and then having an hour-long breakfast, so this meant I would have to cut my routine short. I told him no guarantees, but I would try my best. I then called Hina, asking her what I should do, and she said, "You should go!" The next morning, I prepared to go over to Shiv's house, and as I got closer, I became more and more nervous. By now, I recognized that I liked Shiv and wanted to know him better. As I walked up to his house, his friend recognized me (because of my green hair) and said, "Hey, I've heard a lot about you." Shiv's favorite color is green, so he had immediately noticed me because of my hair. The comment meant that Shiv had been talking about me with his friends, so now I was even more nervous, knowing that he was interested in me.

We ended up breathing next to each other, and I went fully in. The only way to gain the benefits of the Wim Hof practice is to do fast-paced breathing and then hold your breath while constricting muscles to build up oxygen in the body. The technique builds a more robust nervous system, which leads to many positive effects on the body. As we lay next to each other with our bodies almost touching, I could feel the energy between us. It was ecstatic. Once it was time for me to leave, we decided to carpool to the third day of ALA. As we spoke more and shared stories, it became clear that we were connecting. He seemed drawn to me and vice versa. That night we bonded as I shared with him some traumas from my past that I was working to overcome. He felt comfort knowing that he could be vulnerable with me and trust that I would never judge him. We found comfort in each other. After hours of conversation, he dropped me off at my car. I could tell there was this energy between us and that he wanted to kiss me, but we hugged and went our separate ways. I went home, but the exhilaration of that night kept me up. I was jittery; I could not bottle the excitement bursting out of me as my mouth began to hurt from smiling. I was longing to connect with him. The next morning was our last day together, so I sent him a message telling him that I was glad I had met him and was appreciative of our conversation the night before. At the end of the message, I wrote "I love you" because I felt it, meant it, and wanted to see his response. He responded with a lovely message and said, "I love you too!" Ahhhh—those three words sealed the deal. He confirmed what I had experienced with him the entire weekend. I could not have been more excited to see him in person. The day was magical and led to our final graduation, for which my family was in attendance. We chose to stand next to each other and hold hands in a large circle of our peers, and the feeling of being so close seemed natural to me. We ended up sticking together the entire night and were the last two people to leave. We walked toward our cars at the end of the night, and then it was time for one last hug—a hug that would change our lives forever. The hug was not ordinary; it lasted for three hours! The energy between us was profound, and neither of us wanted to let go. It was the most magical experience I have ever had. We held on to each other tightly. I told him I wanted to kiss him, but there was someone else I was romantically interested in who lived in New York. I asked Shiv, "When will I see you?" He said, "Well, you live in LA, and I don't come up there often, so I am not sure when I will see you next." I immediately felt disappointed.

Was this the last time I was going to see him? His response left me saddened because I knew he was important to me, so I suggested that we arrange a time to meet the next day before I drove home to LA. The following day we met at his office, and I was very nervous. There were butterflies in the pit of my stomach that I could not shake off. As I approached his office, I saw his big smile as he waited outside to greet me. I was beaming with happiness, and the smile on my face radiated throughout the entire room. I had imagined that our time would be brief, but we spent several hours together. The time flew by with hugging, laughing, talking, flirting, and being present with each other. We spoke about kids, passions, and family, and I began to imagine my life with him. He told me he had written a letter to me, so I asked him to read it aloud. He shared how he felt about me, how much he cared, and that he wanted to create a life with me. I had never experienced anyone being so clear and forthright about their feelings. He was confident and knew what he wanted, which was me. I was blown away by his loving words and asked to keep the letter (which I still have, along with many other beautiful letters he has written). We realized that we wanted to be with each other. The one thing holding us back was my upcoming trip to visit the other guy that I had feelings for in New York. I had never thought that I would be in this predicament of first, never finding a partner I was interested in, and then, being interested in two people at the same time. What was I supposed to do? I believe it was a test; however, this test was difficult and took a toll on my mental well-being. Shiv was very persistent and firm in his pursuit of me, while I was stuck on pursuing someone else, one of the first guys I had ever been fully vulnerable with. I was chasing the other guy for the wrong reasons, which is not healthy! I told Shiv we should wait to see each other again because I wanted to know that what was between us was real. I thought it was possible that we had been on a high and were living in a bubble, coming out of such an intense experience together. He was not happy but tried to support my space. It was short-lived. We ended up seeing each other again a few days later, and we could not get enough of each other. We wanted to be around each other as often as possible in a long-distance relationship, but I told Shiv I could not be his girlfriend yet. He asked me multiple times, the first being the time at his office, but I wanted space to explore the other relationship and gain clarity around it. It was a stressful time because Shiv was not comfortable with us potentially not being together. I came up against some pressure on his end to cut ties with the other person, but I resisted. Shiv and I saw each other a few more times, one being when we celebrated my birthday together, which made me extremely happy. I believe I was in denial that I could be with such an amazing person who wanted to build a life together. I noticed myself sabotaging the relationship in different ways because of my insecurities. One weekend, I was celebrating my birthday with my family and friends when I fell ill. I ended up in the hospital with an intense UTI that could have easily turned into sepsis. I later learned that UTIs are very detrimental to kidney patients since the bacteria can affect our filtration and end up getting into the bloodstream. Now I am super mindful of having any symptoms and contacting my doctor right away. The infection required me to spend some time in the hospital and cancel my trip to New York. I took this as a sign from the universe to commit to Shiv. He drove up from San Diego to spend the night at the hospital and was with me the entire time during my recovery. I saw how committed he was to me, which meant a lot. He was there when I faced a health setback but never hesitated to commit to fighting any long-term obstacles right by my side. I had exactly what I wanted right in front of me. I had asked the universe for a courageous, worthy man with whom I could build a strong relationship based on trust, communication, and vulnerability. I wanted a mutually supportive and respectful partnership that seeks to create a beautiful family and impact the world, one in which two equals give each other the space to be creative, adventurous, and ambitious without compromising their goals. I have found this in Shiv.

He is beyond a blessing and has the most beautiful soul. From the first moment our eyes met, he accepted me wholly and never once judged me for who I am. I knew I wanted him in my life forever as my best friend and lifelong partner.

He encourages me to never doubt myself and know my worth. He reassures me that I am a powerful, intelligent, and empowered woman. I feel beautiful in my skin when I am with him. I trust him with all that I am; he makes me feel cherished, secure, protected, and confident. He goes out of his way to do the small things to make me feel special. I feel at peace with him, and the world seems like a kinder, more pleasant place. I feel warm and happy being around him; I experience enchantment. He creates space and listens when I vent or ask for feedback. My beliefs, feelings, and values matter to him. He prioritizes me by making the effort to ensure my happiness. His courage empowers me to lead my life with courage. Being with him drives me to be a better version of myself and continue growing spiritually. I am more than willing to compromise and apologize when I am wrong because he elevates my overall mood and gets me excited about the future. I am thrilled to be building a life with him centered on family, community, and impact. I can depend on him to be right by my side through the ebbs and flows of life.

Shiv provides the freedom for me to express myself and encourages me along the way. He affirms my worth and never doubts my capabilities. His unwavering support has given me the confidence to pursue my dreams to bring Antidote and this book into fruition. My long journey to break through my limiting beliefs was well worth it because it led me to Shiv.

I had difficulty realizing Shiv's goodness at first because, for the longest time, I had believed that I would not find a partner who considered me an equal and who I could be completely vulnerable and transparent with. It is rare to have this type of connection and meet someone who completely breaks down the walls you have created around your life.

As Shiv and I continued to spend time together, I enjoyed every moment we had. I still had moments when I was uncomfortable being in a relationship with him because I was still living in a self-sabotaging state of mind. For me, this relationship felt surreal, like this could not be my life because anything I had previously dreamed of was within the limitations I had set. Once my mind began to shift, and I spoke my intentions into existence, the universe started to put things in place for me. Shiv and I entered into a committed relationship at the end of August 2018, after much persistence on his part. I think I gave him such a difficult time becoming his girlfriend because I was so worried about losing myself and potentially being a burden to him. As we continued to see each other, I recognized how much I enjoyed his company, and I was spending more time with him than anyone else I had dated or even my own family. I am sure some of my friends would say they saw less of me in the first few months of my dating Shiv, but it was a crucial time we needed to build our relationship. The beginning of a serious relationship requires a ton of time to learn to understand one another and gauge if this is a relationship worth continuing. Once you have built the base, it becomes easier to manage day-to-day stressors and balance other aspects of your life. It is crucial to have a partner who knows what matters to you and won't bring in unhealthy feelings or thoughts that could harm your relationship. At the beginning my relationship with Shiv faced some obstacles due to the distance between us and the pressures of meeting each other's families. Shiv wanted me to join his family for the holidays, but I was hesitant. My main concern was his family learning about my health condition and whether that would affect how they received me. In Indian culture, families have a great deal of influence on who you date or end up marrying. I had been subjected to judgment in many ways, so I was concerned about whether his family would attempt to change his mind. Shiv and I had discussed this many times. He was adamant that he wanted me in his life, and no one could change that. He first shared this with his father, his brother, and then his mother. It was challenging for me to feel comfortable with him sharing things about my health, but I had faith that it would go well. Fortunately, his family was very welcoming and have been the kindest people.

We had many conversations about our ideal life throughout this time—where we want to live, parenting styles, religion, politics, and so much more! Although we have had our differences, our love and understanding for each other far surpasses them. Over time, we have created a relationship that has supported us in growing and becoming more holistic humans.

I have had many opportunities to stretch or challenge myself within the relationship that I may never have had otherwise; for example, I come from a more conservative family where relationships are not spoken about unless you are at the point of considering marriage; otherwise, the person would not be introduced to your family. In Shiv's case, his parents are more open and have met past girlfriends. This is just one example of the differences in our upbringings and family dynamics. My parents and I were fairly open with each other; however, there were specific unspoken rules that I never challenged or discussed. Shiv was very adamant about meeting my parents and me connecting with his entire family. For him this was a sign of transparency, which is one of his values. I understood his stance; however, I had cultural norms to manage. Indian culture is more conservative around dating, but there is a double standard for dating as a female. I recognized this norm, but Shiv struggled to accept it because for him it was merely about having the courage to speak up. I realized that I had difficulty speaking up and voicing my truth; however, I felt I was not supported due to the cultural complexity involved. It was never a matter of fear or trust but a point of understanding. If people focus on communication and open themselves up to hear and understand others, we can find common ground. Ultimately, I told my parents about Shiv of my own accord. This conversation happened without any pressure to share because I knew I could only do this if it were authentic. My parents were supportive and reacted very happily. All they wanted was for me to be happy and to be a part of my relationship. They did not pressure me to progress the relationship, which I may have had assumptions about before sharing. I had decided beforehand that I would not be attached to their response, nor would I take on any pressure to do something that was not aligned with me. I wanted to do things at my own pace by recognizing the intention behind my action. I knew that if I felt pressured to do something inauthentic, it would result in guilt and stress. After telling my parents about Shiv, I witnessed myself become fully present in our relationship. I was no longer living in partial secrecy. My parents' first question was, "Does Shiv know about your health condition?" This question might sound ridiculous, but it has always been a genuine concern of theirs. They know how Indian culture is and how judgmental people can be in general, so they wanted to make sure he was committed and knew what would be involved in a serious relationship with me. As he grew closer to my family and vice versa, we recognized that our relationship was getting serious enough for me to consider moving to be closer to him. After a year and a half together, I decided to leave Los Angeles and move to San Diego. It was stressful for me to come to this decision because I was worried about work and the uncertainty of developing a new community that I could lean on for support. There was also a fear of being emotionally dependent on Shiv and the need to overcome my first living experience in San Diego. The move would require me to create a new association with the city after my grim, short-lived time at UCSD eight years prior. I was nervous about placing too much pressure on Shiv to make my experience of San Diego pleasant this time around. I was moving there for our relationship first and my career second, so I counted on this to go well. Shiv deserved my full commitment to giving San Diego another chance.

CHAPTER 14

TRANSFORMATION

C ommitting to San Diego hugely influenced the transformation work that followed. At the time, I was fixated on the expectations that I had set for myself with the move. I compared myself to others and had false definitions of success and accomplishment, which I later learned to rewire through activities and therapy. I thought I would immediately launch Antidote and thus lead a successful life. This could not be done quickly, as I had a narrow definition of success that focused only on career, not health or relationships (family, personal, and community). This mindset was unhealthy, so I learned to redefine many societal and personal pressures/norms. I realized that I was not acknowledging what I had accomplished thus far because I was constantly comparing myself to others. The comparisons led to my placing judgment and stress upon myself to meet these extreme expectations. Shiv has always supported me and my passion for helping and advocating for kidney patients. He was proactive in introducing me to his network and giving me resources to launch my start-up, but something still held me back. I was passionate about Antidote, but I was losing why I wanted to launch Antidote in the first place. I recognized that I was attaching my worth and expectations of myself to the success of Antidote. This attachment was unhealthy, so I began to question the limiting beliefs that came up for me.

I developed a deep frustration for these circumstances because I had a plan going into this. As I felt the walls caving in, I went inward and permitted myself to focus on healing. I say healing because I am now in a healthy place in my life where I can fit the puzzle pieces together and "assemble" myself by being grounded in my beliefs, having faith, and knowing who I am. This journey has allowed me to gain deep clarity on my why: my purpose on this earth. Participating in different activities and gaining tools throughout the years (see the resources section at the end of the book) has allowed me to progress in the direction of trusting myself and having the confidence to lead myself to accomplish my goals. It has brought mindfulness to the forefront to support me with setting intentions in the face of judgment and discouragement. I have connected back to my purpose or calling, and the clarity around it has come through my spiritual journey and healing.

I say spiritual journey because I entered a more elevated state of better understanding myself. It was a process that I had not expected; however, it has been a gratifying experience. Heading into my move, I was anxious and fearful of the unknowns that I would be exposed to. I had some expectations around what I would be doing once I moved, and they turned out not to be accurate. I was still attached to expectations that others had for me and that I set for myself. I thought I was ready to jump into my start-up, Antidote, and be at any and every social event, but this was by no means the case. After speaking with my therapist, I recognized that enjoying the new space I was in would be crucial to adjusting to life in San Diego. I had never lived alone, but I had roommates during a few short periods at college. It was vital for me to be by myself to discover who I am without others around me for the first time.

Being around people can lead to our taking on their emotions, anxieties, likes, dislikes, and so forth. I wanted to strip myself of any external influences to build who I am— Hiral—and gain a stronger understanding of myself at my core. This understanding would support me in showing up authentically in all aspects of my life! The timing set me up for introspection because a month after I moved, COVID-19 lockdowns began in California. I had already implemented certain habits and begun activities such as meditating, reading, writing, and self-help work, in addition to practicing spirituality with a focus on patience and presence. I was also honing in on my diet, as I had had difficulty gaining weight ever since my transplant surgery. I was now aware of some food allergies contributing to my fatigue and brain fog, which slowed my progress. As I sat on the living room floor, the overwhelm of mental and physical frustration overpowered my train of thought and I began crying. I had experienced this before and recognized that I was on the verge of another mindset shift. I spoke with Shiv, who is very experienced at creating a framework for breakthrough activities, and he suggested that I begin with a values activity. I tested out the values activity for a few weeks before creating a fantastic framework that worked for me. It is the foundation of how I now choose to live my life and how I make decisions. In Section IV, I have listed the resources that I found beneficial. My hope is that this will help you create your breakthroughs. Once I had a set of concrete values, I had the confidence to then follow my intuition and use the values I was aligned with to support me in goal planning and understanding the psychology of why I make certain decisions. This insight helped me create new routines around my diet, meditation, prayer, and exercise. I integrated many tools that I had used previously while also implementing new tools to support my journey to become my own expert. These healthy habits gave me the structure to reduce my stress and create a calm mind, which impacted my body for the better. I observed fewer sleepless nights, a reduction in bloating and inflammation, increased energy, and most importantly, interest in eating a clean diet. I felt inclined to eat healthier foods that did not irritate my body. It was a complete shift from the hectic, unhealthy, stressful life back in Los Angeles that I had once flourished in. With this positive momentum, I began to see my body change. I was now 10+ pounds heavier than when I moved, which meant I had finally gained the 10 pounds I had worked toward for the past ten years. It happened within a matter of months. This example is the power of healing your body through your mind. Once you go through these activities, you will understand how important loving and accepting yourself is for your mental and physical health. It can also have a radical effect on your longevity, so I truly encourage you to take your time as you work through each activity.

I had done personal development work through the years; however, there was much more that I wanted to process now, using the tools I gained inside and outside of the academy. As my healing continued, I learned more about myself by unraveling traumas, fears, and emotions that went back to when I was a child. The activities I participated in took place over multiple hours and sometimes days. It took a ton of mental energy, but I needed to do this because I wanted to reclaim my life and rejoice again. During the process of self-discovery, I focused on various tests and completed multiple activities to understand what drives me, where my purpose lies, and how I view the world. I know that understanding myself and being confident in my capabilities will ultimately release me from the shackles of limiting myself when I should instead recognize my full potential. In writing this book and working on the different activities, I want others to know that they should never limit themselves because of their circumstances. We deserve to fulfill our purpose, and it all begins with understanding ourselves and becoming empowered. In the next section, I have shared all of the activities that I completed and broken down the process so that others can hopefully gain as much value from them as I have. In addition, the books listed have given me more context in understanding myself and learning about communication with myself and others.

Through these experiences, I began to rebuild myself by living from a place of confidence, self-worth, courage, honesty, forgiveness, and compassion for others and myself.

I was now able to work through the emotions and traumas that had been blocking my growth. I learned to trust myself to only participate in activities that give me energy and are aligned with my values. I realized that I am in command of my destiny.

I also learned that advocacy, support, and empowerment are very important to me. These are all fundamental values that are the basis of why I decided to launch Antidote (http://antidotehealth.io). Support and empowerment help us thrive, so why go through this journey alone? There are so many others who share similar experiences and understand the pain, so it's good to get vulnerable by sharing your story and advocating for yourself and others. We each have unique qualities that differentiate us from others; we are not the same. Our experiences can provide others the support they need to manage their health. This is why I felt compelled to write this book, so my story can encourage others to share their stories and experiences of resiliency in the face of adversity. I also want people to understand that they are not alone; many people share similar experiences. Our lives do not have to be diminished because of our health. We are resilient and will get through this together.

I see it as good being generated to support people in knowing themselves and having the awareness to go forward with their lives. I recognize how impactful this work has been for me in processing my healing phase. Writing this book has supported me in getting aligned with why I want to start Antidote, which is to create a nonjudgmental space that promotes a comprehensive approach to well-being and empowers people living with kidney disease to develop supportive relationships. This book is for those who want to be heard, share their stories, and reclaim their lives.

I had always wanted to write a book and share my life story within the kidney community, other health communities, and my loved ones. The book is something that I can pass on to others—something to be remembered by and allow my legacy to continue. During the writing process, I learned to let go of being analytical and judgmental around my writing skills and questioning the significance of my story. I recognize that my story is no longer mine; it now belongs to everyone else who reads this book. In sharing here, I have given myself permission to speak openly and be vulnerable. Writing this book has been the commencement of the next phase of my life, now that I have recognized my full potential. I have gained confidence in myself and recognized my voice in this world. I am attaining all that I have dreamed of: finding a partner in Shiv, building confidence and trust in myself, sharing my journey through this book, and launching Antidote, all with the loving support of Shiv, my family, and my dearest friends. I am now in a space to lead with love to create the change I want to see in this world. I have reclaimed my identity apart from CKD and past traumas to experience true freedom and confidence. So I ask you this: how often do you do things that make you happy? Do you even know what makes you happy? Can you share with others your hopes and dreams for the future? These questions can feel daunting, especially to someone who has never considered them. I asked myself these questions numerous times before I allowed myself to reflect on and answer them. I became dissatisfied with my circumstances and woke up every day anxious, on edge, and dreading the long day ahead. I had accepted this as my reality because I was confused about what I wanted and made decisions based on fear and guilt. For many years, others told me how I should be living and what would make me happy. When I would share my goals, some people would question them, which triggered me to suppress my thoughts. I spiraled, questioning whether the people closest to me were supportive. Did they want the best for me? I doubted others' intentions and I doubted myself. The thing was, I honestly did not know what I wanted. How was it that my life felt like it was falling apart? How was I completely unsettled and confused about my direction in life when I had amazing opportunities ahead of me? The truth was that I was living my life for everyone else— to satisfy everyone but myself. I was holding on to a tiny thread of my own identity. I unraveled with days of crying and fits of anger over any tension or indiscretion. I had no tools to de-stress or overcome the slightest setbacks; how would I ever manage uncertainty? This was a vast undertaking, but I knew that if I took the time to use these resources (see Section IV) to build myself up at the core, then I would prosper. After years of being influenced by others, I took the uncomfortable leap into soul-searching. If you find yourself unsatisfied with your circumstances and relationships, then I encourage you to reclaim who you are at the core. I ask you to take a stand for yourself by permitting yourself to elevate your state of being.

Our mindset is powerful and influences our actions, so we can take action by challenging our thoughts and creating a new, healthy mind frame to live by. This shift begins with asking questions and processing emotions, which may be uncomfortable but is entirely worth the energy. You will better understand your authentic self through these activities, which will help you on your path to understanding your purpose and your why. I encourage you to embrace the present moment and open yourself up to uncertainty. You will experience freedom—true freedom! It is attainable, and I want to provide this to you. Do not wait any longer to reclaim your identity. I invite you to take a stand for yourself by joining me on this journey. It all begins with one activity to change your life, so what are you waiting for? Your time is now, so take the first step!

Join me in sharing your story and experience with the activities at http://antidotehealth.io/?post_type=forum. Begin your journey to embrace the beauty within with the support of this book and Antidote—your ally in health!

PART IV
RESOURCES AND ACTIVITIES

A GUIDE TO CREATING BREAKTHROUGHS

This portion of the book provides materials and activities that have supported me at various points in my life in establishing structure, gaining clarity, and overcoming limiting beliefs. I believe they can also support you on your journey in developing accountability, setting goals, releasing unwanted energy, creating boundaries, aligning with values, understanding yourself, making choices, and living in authenticity.

Many of the current anxieties, fears, and stressors we experience come from a combination of what others experience and what we experience. At birth we are pure, meaning without any trauma, discontent, anxiety, stress, or fear. As we get older, not only our personal trauma but the traumas of people we encounter (teachers, parents, siblings, coaches, counselors, neighbors, friends, cousins, etc.) are put on us. This creates many layers of trauma that we try to manage daily. Most traumas are not ours; however, we take them on, and that is where boundaries are crossed. To take back our power, we get to relinquish traumas and anxieties, especially those of others.

The goal in using these resources and participating in these activities is to find what works for you and the support you are looking for at the moment. Day by day, we encounter many breakdowns, and in those breakdowns there is something for us to reflect on. With the breakdowns come breakthroughs— the realizations. The realizations are essential for processing emotions and taking action on the information you have gained awareness around.

To create breakthroughs work on activities that challenge you, and create unwarranted emotions. Once we get out of our comfort zones, growth begins. As we allow ourselves to lean into our fears and anxieties, we peel away the layers of the deeper, underlying issues at hand. It is a tough decision to allow yourself to gain awareness and no longer live in a state of avoidance; however, our mental and physical well-being may decline if we continue in avoidance, which does not bring us joy. Being mindful and living in authenticity will lead to joy.

BOOK RECOMMENDATIONS

Please research these books on your own, so you can choose those that resonate with you. These are just suggestions from personal reads that I have enjoyed and found supportive in understanding myself and the world around me.

- *The Happiness Project* by Gretchen Rubin
- *Talking to Strangers* by Malcolm Gladwell
- *Stillness Speaks* by Eckhart Tolle
- *Quiet* by Susan Cain
- *Start with Why* by Simon Sinek
- *The Untethered Soul* by Michael A. Singer
- *Waking Up* by Sam Harris
- *Antifragile* by Nassim Nicholas Taleb
- *The Road Back to You* by Ian Morgan Cron
- *The Coddling of the American Mind* by Greg Lukianoff
- *The Power of Positive Thinking* by Norman Vincent Peale
- *Loving What Is* by Byron Katie
- *Creative Visualization* by Shakti Gawain
- *No Excuses!* by Brian Tracy
- *The Artist's Way* by Julia Cameron

ACCOUNTABILITY/SUPPORT APPS

Please enjoy these free apps and resources to better support you in maintaining or creating new healthy habits for your daily routine.

- Insight Timer (meditation)
- Libby (public library resource, free books/audibles)
- WHM (Wim Hof breathing)
- AllTrails (outdoor hiking)
- WOOP (reframing, creating small attainable goals)
- ReWi (inputting activity)
- Reminder (sets reminders for activities/daily routine)
- Clock (create timers and/or alarms for daily actions)
- My Fitness Pal (meal tracker)
- Water Tracker (daily water reminder/tracker)

Activities

Here is a list of activities for you to consider. Everyone is different, so choose activities that are in alignment with what you would like to accomplish.

- Self-reflection
- Reframing Activity
- Personal Values Exploration
- Personality/Behavior Exercises:
- Social Capital
- Energizers or Energy Drainers
- Clearing Conversations/Forgiveness
- Setting Healthy Boundaries
- Mindfulness
- Goal Planning/Accountability
- Meditation, Breathing Exercises, and Body Scanning

As we move forward with the reflection activities, I ask that you only participate when you have a calm, focused mind to get the most out of the exercises. If you do not find yourself in a calm headspace, then take a moment to take some deep breaths and meditate to align with your intention for the activity. Have fun and enjoy the adventure!

"One way to make the most out of life is to look upon it as an adventure"
—William Feather

SELF-REFLECTION

Introspection: to learn more about your fundamental nature and essence. This requires using a means or process to assess yourself—your character, actions, and motives, which leads to growth and self-understanding. The methods can include meditation, journaling, participating in an activity, and talking to others. This activity came about when I had just moved to San Diego and was overwhelmed by the thought of "What will I do next?" I found myself spiraling down an anxiety-filled hole, but this activity supported me in putting everything into perspective. Once I meditated on the list of questions, I wrote a letter describing my ideal life, living in alignment with myself without any fears. I now reflect on this activity when I experience anxiety to get back in alignment with myself.

Before you begin the self-reflection process, I suggest that you identify a list of essential questions that you are interested in gaining a deeper understanding of— inspiring questions.

Here are some examples:

- Am I living true to myself?
- Am I waking up in the morning ready to take on the day?
- Am I taking care of myself physically?
- What am I scared of?
- Am I holding on to something I need to let go of?
- What matters most in my life?

Once you create your list of questions, take some time to either meditate on them and allow different thoughts to come up for you or begin writing or talking about them, allowing your mind to bring this information to the forefront of your brain. It is important not to jump to conclusions with the knowledge that comes to you but to understand it and continue reflecting on the question. It is essential to then use the information you gained from reflection and take action.

Here are a few ways to take action:

- Create affirmations particular to your needs, i.e., I am a confident woman.
- Manifest through intention and visualization, i.e., create a vision board for the year covering a range of interests and reflecting your hopes and dreams.
- Write a letter describing your ideal day and life.
- Keep a daily journal to write out all of your thoughts.
- Take yourself out on a date, i.e., go for a walk alone or treat yourself to a movie.

The aspects of manifestation and visualization tie into introspection because they use the imagination, mental images, and the power of thoughts to attract the energy to make dreams and goals come true. It is imperative to keep consistent positive visual pictures in your mind, so that your energy can be channeled toward those particular goals. The visuals will lead you to take action and continue to stay focused on attaining what you want out of life. In the process you get to clear the resistance by trusting yourself and surrendering to the universe.

Step 1: Get clear about what your desires are by focusing on how you will feel by attaining them.

Step 2: Allow the universe's positive energy to flow through your thoughts by meditating on your desires.

Step 3: Take action by living in alignment with the desires you seek, i.e., if you want romance, then begin with loving yourself —take yourself out on a solo date.

REFRAMING ACTIVITY

Reframing is a way to change how you are experiencing something, thus changing your understanding of it. It can reduce stress and promote a greater sense of peace and control in your life. Our minds are sponges that retain information, especially our subconscious, which takes our thoughts as factual. It is imperative to rewire our brains (i.e., reprogram them through intentional habits) to create the positive outcomes we seek. Doing this consistently over some time will produce a positive, habitual change in the way you think and the actions you take. I realized that I was completely neglecting my health because of work. I wanted to shift my focus to my health, so this reframing activity supported reframing my thoughts so that I am reminded to nourish my body. This tool can be used for various situations, but I recommend you try it with small day-to-day tasks first so you can gain practice and lose judgment around the result of the action.

Example: I don't want to take a lunch break right now because I have a lot of work to do.

Reframe: I will nourish my body by having lunch so that I have the energy to complete my work.

Example: I do not want to meditate because I do not have time this morning. I have other things to do.

Reframe: I will take 10 minutes of my morning to meditate to be calmer and more productive throughout my day.

I would suggest writing down the situation or problem, how you feel about it, and then create reframes to shift your perspective. Eventually, you will get to a place where your mind will do it naturally as soon as you encounter a negative emotion. The focus is on finding the good in a situation or a more positive outcome, so we become less affected by negative situations. The activity is not a one-time fix; it requires active participation and consistency, but you will recognize the difference fairly quickly. The key is to practice, practice, practice!

PERSONAL VALUES EXPLORATION

This exercise is significant because personal values reflect how you show up in your life, and they are specific to your needs— the things that are important to you. They help us to grow, develop, and create the future we want to enjoy. Our values inform our thoughts, words, and actions. Finally, the choices we make reflect our values, and they are always directed toward a specific purpose.

We are strictly focused on personal values here; however, you can do the same exercise for a relationship, business, society, and so forth. I completed this particular activity by listing my values on my glass closet door. This supported me in visualizing the values and seeing them each morning before I finalized my list. There are many ways to conduct this activity, but here are the steps I used to explore and rank values.

First, sit down with pen and paper and write down your definition of value. Please define it in your own words. My definition of value is something that gives me energy.

Second, write down as many values that come to your mind. Make a list like the one I have provided below. If you are having difficulty, then take some time to research words that resonate with you.

Here is a small pool of words to reflect on:

Adventure	Abundance	Creativity
Respect	Passion	Honesty
Health	Service	Intimacy
Empathy	Fairness	Integrity
Support	Family	Spirituality
Joy	Friendship	Forgiveness
Freedom	Ambition	Growth
Confidence	Loyalty	Patience
Humor	Compassion	Inner Harmony
Trust	Gratitude	Kindness
Curiosity	Tradition	Self-worth
Courage	Self-control	Vision
Care	Presence	Passion

Once you have completed the step of writing down the values that resonate with you, take some time to reflect before moving on to Step 3. The next step will require you to sort the values you have listed into five categories. The categories do not need to be named, and the values are not required to be evenly distributed. Third, begin categorizing values on a new sheet of paper by identifying the values that are similar or alike. Put similar values in the same category. The point of this is to eventually get down to five values by slowly narrowing your choices.

After your list is complete, I suggest you reflect on it for a few hours or days to get familiar with the values. There are creative ways of doing this, such as posting the list on your refrigerator, writing it on a whiteboard, or the way I did it, which was to write them all on my closet door using a dry erase marker.

Once you feel comfortable with your list, begin defining each value in your own words. This helps you understand your reasons for choosing the word and why it is important to you. If the definition is short, simple, or vague, this does not mean that it is not important to you; it just means that it may not be as significant to you as the other values. At some point you will recognize a pattern with the values you chose. Values can change over time based on our needs, so do not overthink this activity and feel that the values must be absolute.

As you begin to process the words and shorten your list, the words not described or least described can be the first words removed from your new list. Eventually, you should have a list of 10 to 15 words that you can then rank in importance to you from 1 to 10 (1 being the most important).

Once completed, you now have your list of values that will be important to reflect on, especially if you feel that your actions are not aligned with them. It is essential to recognize that when you are not happy about something, it is because you are out of alignment with your values.

PERSONALITY/BEHAVIOR TESTS

I have provided a list of tests below that can support you in understanding your personality or behavior. This is crucial because your personality influences what type of career you choose, how you make decisions, what matters to you, how you communicate, and so much more! The insight can also support you in better understanding others based on their personalities to communicate more effectively.

The first test we will focus on is the quadrant personality test, also known as the DISC personality test, which supports you in understanding your dominant behavior style. It could be that you display some traits of different styles. Still, the goal is to be able to style flex, utilizing different communication or personality styles in particular situations. Ideally, you would want to embody all four styles. This is not to say that any particular personality is better than the others; the goal is to embody all styles to access them in different situations. This activity supported me in gaining awareness around what motivated my actions. I was unaware of how I was coming off to people; for example, when my brother first joined the family business, I was unwilling to give him any responsibilities because I was fearful of him doing something wrong and felt that I was the best person to do the job. It was the controller in me. If I had understood then how to shift out of my autocratic, controlling ways, I would have been a better support system for my brother to learn the family business.

FORMAL
(Task Oriented)

		Con trolling	Ana lyzing	
1				
2				
3		Pro moting	Sup porting	
4				
	A	B	C	D

DOMINANT (Extrovert)

EASY-GOING (Introvert)

INFORMAL
(People Oriented)

Here are some insights into the strengths and drawbacks of each leadership style in this model.

Controller

Beneficial traits: Take charge, determined, decisive, results-oriented, efficient

<u>Unhelpful traits</u>: Autocratic, insensitive, impatient, over-controlling, inattentive listening

Supporter

<u>Beneficial traits</u>: Team player, friendly, good listener, relationship-oriented, conscientious

<u>Unhelpful traits</u>: Overly tolerant, unassertive, nonconfrontational, overly driven to please

Promoter

<u>Beneficial traits</u>: Stimulating, goal-driven, enthusiastic, innovative, risk-taker

<u>Unhelpful traits</u>: Inattention to planning, ego-driven, undisciplined, inadequate follow-up

Analyzer

<u>Beneficial traits</u>: Thorough, detailed, rational, organized, good planner

<u>Unhelpful traits</u>: Indecisive, overly detailed, aloof, risk averse, intuitively challenged

To learn your quadrant personality, click the link below to take the free 10-minute test.

https://marvelous-crafter-2297.ck.page/e01578e20b.

The second test I recommend is the Myers-Briggs personality test. Many people have used this test in and out of academic settings.

ISTJ	ISFJ	INFJ	INTJ
ISTP	ISFP	INFP	INTP
ESTP	ESFP	ENFP	ENTP
ESTJ	ESFJ	ENFJ	ENTJ

It is well established after 70+ years in circulation. The test has 16 different personality types, which are expressed with four different letters. The four letters reflect four categories: favorite world (introversion vs. extroversion), information (sensing vs. intuition), decisions (thinking vs. feeling), and structure (judging vs. perceiving). All of this information is explained on myersbriggs.org, where you can take the test and get immediate, detailed information and insight into your personality type. In this chart, you will find an image of the 16 personality types that show the different four-letter combinations possible for this test.

The third test listed, the Enneagram, includes nine personality types (labeled 1–9) that describe how people perceive their surroundings and process their emotions. The test provides insight into strengths, weaknesses, likes, and dislikes. Remember that a test will never fully sum up who you are and should be taken simply as insight to better support your relationships and goals. The nine different Enneagram types are The Perfectionist (1), The Helper (2), The Performer (3), The Romantic (4), The Investigator (5), The Loyalist (6), The Enthusiast (7), The Challenger (8), and The Peacemaker (9).

The types can be briefly described as follows:

(1) The Perfectionist: They have a high expectation of others and themselves. They will get the job done but may be too critical at times.

(2) The Helper: They are generous in their efforts and mean well, but they can rely on other people's need for them by tying it to their self-worth.

(3) The Performer: They are optimistic and resilient but focus too much on their image.

(4) The Romantic: They are sensitive, creative, and emotionally honest but uncertain about who they are.

(5) The Investigator: They prefer to observe and collect knowledge in various subjects but can be viewed as aloof.

(6) The Loyalist: They have a liking for structure and security but suffer from anxiety.

(7) The Enthusiast: They are spontaneous, adventurous, and always interested in a good time, but they tend to avoid processing pain or other unwanted emotions.

(8) The Challenger: They are independent, outspoken advocates but can be confrontational and aggressive.

(9) The Peacemaker: They are natural mediators, flexible and unselfish, but can become unhealthily dependent on others.

The descriptions I provided are a brief overview of each personality. In addition to taking the Enneagram test, I suggest reading the book *The Road Back to You* by Ian Cron and Suzanne Stabile because it is very insightful and breaks down each personality type into the characteristics of healthy, unhealthy, or average individuals of that type. The test I took is provided on truity.com. Use it as a tool, along with the other tests and activities, to better understand yourself. I know you will find it helpful and informative. Good luck!

SOCIAL CAPITAL

The concept of social capital is vital for developing mutually supportive relationships. The ability to cultivate mutually supportive relationships is central to professional success and personal well-being. The mutual goodwill, trust, cooperation, and influence you develop through your relationships help you gain the resources you need to add value to your life. The definition of social capital is the resources you have access to through your personal and professional relationships.[1] These resources include things like information, contacts, opportunities (such as job leads), mentoring, money, encouragement, and support for your ideas. It is crucial to realize that no one succeeds alone. This activity will support you in developing a visual representation of your social connections. These connections include the type and amount of social capital you have access to. Building a network that is mutually supportive and valuable to you and others will impact your success. It is important to have a diverse, open network in order to have more information and resources available to accomplish your goals. I have always been aware that your network is your net worth; however, I had never done an in-depth analysis of my relationships. After participating in Dr. Caproni's Science of Success course, I gained a practical and straightforward process for understanding my network. This activity has supported me in building relationships that are conducive to my success. Here is a detailed breakdown of the sociogram activity to illustrate your social capital.

Create a sociogram by placing your name in a circle in the middle of a piece of paper. Then list the names of people you have connected with in the past six to eight months that have supported you in some capacity. Group these into categories such as work, family, community, etc.

Once completed, begin to draw a line between people who know each other within and across the different categories. Then place a star next to the people you know very well.

Once you have finished this task, reflect on the number of lines within your diagram. If you have many lines on your diagram showing connections among many people within your circles, this indicates that you have a less diversified network. This means you have access to fewer types of resources since similar resources are what join the people who are connected on the diagram. The goal is to have many diverse relationships separate from connections to others within your circle so you can access resources that are not already spoken for by others in your network.

With this insight you can begin to connect with people you want to include in your network and strategically build relationships to accomplish your goals. Try different techniques that are conducive to your personality. Whether you are introverted or extroverted, there are many ways to connect and build social networks. I identify as an introvert who can function as an extrovert in larger settings, although doing so is exhausting. After taking the Meyers-Briggs test, I better understood my personality type and socializing preferences. This has improved my approach to networking. Introverts appreciate solitude over large crowds, so if you find it uncomfortable to attend a large networking event, there are other ways to make networking work for you.

Tip #1: Take your networking online by establishing a presence on LinkedIn and begin interacting with people in your field. This is a great way to virtually network without having to strike up conversations with strangers.

Tip #2: Prepare for an in-person networking event by researching some attendees you would like to connect with and creating a few opening questions to ease your nerves. This will help give you the confidence to approach strangers.

As for extroverts, interacting with new people comes naturally to you; however, here are some ideas to support more effective approaches to networking.

Tip #1: Be present with the person you are speaking with because people will notice if your eyes are wandering to others in the crowd. Try to focus on intentional networking versus counting the number of connections you make.

Tip #2: Ask open-ended questions, which allow the other person to engage in the conservation. We want the interaction to be genuine, not one-sided. So speak—but also listen.

Who you know is just as important as what you know. Be

mindful of sharing your knowledge, skills, and expertise with others, so you can build mutually beneficial relationships.

ENERGIZERS OR ENERGY DRAINERS

It is important to reflect on people in your circle that are either energizers or energy drainers. I am not telling you to go and cut off relationships in your life. Instead, reflect on the current people in your life, especially those you spend the most time with, and consider how much energy they either give to or take from you. Your success is dependent on giving little to no time to people who are draining energy from you, especially if you are an introvert. I first used this activity when I became dissatisfied with specific relationships and social settings that were no longer serving me. I could no longer withstand having my energy drained by people, so this activity supported me in prioritizing mutually supportive, energizing relationships. The activity had an immensely positive effect on my life. Imagine one person in your life who is draining so much energy from you that no longer being in a relationship with them would change your productivity and happiness levels for the better. Write down the names of people in your life and "grade" them one by one. Take a look at the people who give you energy; acknowledge that and continue building those relationships. Then look at the people who are the opposite (energy drainers) and reflect. Ask yourself how they are draining you, what boundaries can you create around them, and where you prioritize that relationship. Do this for each person on the list. Then, moving forward, lead with what you have learned from this exercise. There may be family members on the "energy drainers" list; however, do not let this prevent you from completing this activity. There are ways to change the dynamics of relationships with family members, such as implementing boundaries. The activity is slightly uncomfortable and may seem mean or judgmental. I thought this at first, but it is very beneficial in the long run. We all have people in our lives that fit one category or the other, so use this as a means to conserve energy for yourself and direct it toward the people you genuinely want to give your energy to.

CLEARING CONVERSATIONS/FORGIVENESS

A clearing conversation may be defined as the act of engaging in dialogue with someone to discuss any ill feelings or negative emotions harbored that caused the relationship to change or end. It can also include being triggered or offended by someone. The purpose is to establish a common understanding of trust. There are five key elements in conducting a proper clearing conversation. These elements ensure that all parties agree to participate in the conversation, and it will be a safe space for each party to express their perspective on the situation. My experience with clearing conversations began in my teens. I had such a conversation with Hina, when she kicked me out of her car one day and left me stranded to walk the few miles home. This action was because of an argument we had about her then-boyfriend. Years later, I practiced clearing conversations with a few close friends that I had conflicts with. These friends were unfamiliar with the concept, so I took the lead in creating a space to clear miscommunication to allow us to move forward. Unfortunately, some of those relationships did not make it, but

I was appreciative that I had spoken my truth and gained forgiveness for myself and the other individual. Clearing conversations are possible for any relationship in your life that you want to release from resentment.

First, set your intention about who you want to reach out to and the conversation you would like to have. This step is important because your mindset at that moment can affect the tone, words, and form of your communication. It is important to be calm, centered, and lead with love.

Second, reach out to the person and ask their permission to discuss something that has been weighing on you concerning your relationship with them. If the person agrees, then continue with the following steps listed below.

Third, acknowledge the person for speaking with you, then acknowledge the response to the topic being cleared by using statements such as "I acknowledge you for ___."

Fourth, take responsibility for your emotions and your part in the situation by using statements such as "I felt," or "The story I created when you said 'XYZ' was that my friendship with you was not important." You can say you are sorry or find other words to convey that you take full ownership of your part.

Fifth, you can ask if they have any requests for you moving forward. If they don't, you can state any requests you would like to make based on the result you desire from the conversation. This is a way to create a shared understanding of what was discussed, so you can both move on from there.

Once you have engaged in the clearing conversation, take time to digest the information and address any other emotions tied to the situation. No matter how the conversation ends, take time to forgive yourself and the other person by actively saying, "I forgive myself, and I forgive ___." It can be challenging to seek forgiveness; however, once you begin practicing forgiveness or the act of letting go, you will find the process much easier in the future. Also, forgiveness leaves your mind, body, and soul at peace because the energy you were harboring has now been released. Our bodies are affected by holding on to emotions, thoughts, etc., so be kind to yourself by participating in these conversations to find ultimate freedom and peace. We do not have power over other people's feelings, nor are we responsible for their emotions, so all we can do is take responsibility for our feelings and move forward from there.

Trust yourself and your intention; you've got this!

SETTING HEALTHY BOUNDARIES

Boundaries can be mental, emotional, physical, material, or sexual. They are the rules and principles you live by that determine what you will or will not be responsible for. The purpose of setting healthy boundaries is to protect your identity and define your individuality. The advantages of healthy boundaries are good mental health, avoidance of burnout, developing identity, good emotional health, autonomy, and influence on others.[1] When boundaries are not healthy, people tend to harbor resentment, anger, anxiety, and guilt. Ultimately, people will experience burnout from the constant "doing" for others and lack of energy reserve for themselves. Setting boundaries can be incredibly difficult for someone who is codependent. Because they put others' feelings and needs before their own, they may fear that setting boundaries could jeopardize their relationships. I have been required to set healthy boundaries, especially with family since my work and personal life were mixed together when I was working with my parents; for example, emotions were heightened when I decided to leave the family business after ten years and move to San Diego to launch Antidote. My parents were displeased because I no longer would be available to support them in different capacities. I was their go-to helper when they needed tech support, medical appointments scheduled, bank deposits made, and almost anything else. My parents had become very used to me helping any time they asked. I was fearful of saying no due to potentially jeopardizing my relationship with them and causing them distress (although I now know that I am not responsible for their emotions). This fear led me to harbor resentment toward them for my lack of time to do things that I enjoyed. This example is one of many that required me to step into my power and speak up by establishing healthy boundaries.

Setting boundaries is a learned behavior, so if you have not experienced other people valuing your boundaries or seeing others' boundaries as valuable, it will take time to learn. You have a right to say no and for people to respect your answer. It could mean changing plans, canceling commitments, not helping someone if you do not have the time, or conserving energy for yourself. In the previous example, a healthy boundary would be to say, "No, I cannot support you right now. I will let you know when I am free to help you." You most likely will get a reaction, but it is crucial to stay firm and not make it personal. Your boundary is not up for discussion. Now let's look at how to set healthy boundaries.

First, assess if you have any existing healthy boundaries or lack them in different aspects of your life.

Second, say no if you are asked to do something that you are not comfortable with or that is not aligned with you. The point is to be firm by saying no and explicitly stating why the boundary is important to you. When you say no, you get to be clear about the reason so the person better understands what is important to you. It is crucial to take action in accordance with your words; otherwise, people may test your resolve.

Third, make the boundary about you and not about the other person; for example, instead of saying, "Stop asking me for help," say, "I am busy for the next few hours, but I will let you know when I am available."

The key is to be honest with people about your boundaries and avoid making assumptions or crossing others' boundaries. Also, do not judge yourself or others on the boundaries that are set because we are all different. The key to setting boundaries is to decide what you want from the various relationships in your life, set boundaries based on those desires, and then be clear with yourself and others about your boundaries. It is an uncomfortable process to establish strong, healthy boundaries, but this activity is crucial to your emotional and mental well-being.

> *"Boundaries need to be communicated first verbally and then with action."*
> —*Dr. Henry Cloud* [2]

MINDFULNESS

Mindfulness is the practice of presence in the here and now—reality. It requires one to pause judgment and detach from mourning the past or fantasizing about the future. In doing so, you will no longer attach your happiness to the moments when things happen for you versus to you. I have become very focused on mindfulness since it is one of my top six values. During my move, there were many moments when I was fixated on the past or future but completely detached from the present (reality). An example of my fantasizing about the future would be "I will be happy when I launch Antidote." This mindset will leave you with fear or anxiety during the time you're waiting and if things do not go as planned. These emotions can be avoided by focusing on what you can do now versus in the future. Another example that I experienced was lamenting about how life was exciting when I spent hours on the tennis court, and how I long to play at that level again. These are examples of what Giridhari Das calls the "fantasy paradigm."[1]

In the fantasy paradigm, people become fixated on what

others have and start comparing their lives to others. This fixation leads to a cycle of jealousy toward those who possess things that they want. Furthermore, possessions then become the thing that happiness gets tied to.

So, if you catch yourself in a desiring mind frame, saying, "I would like to have ____," then you are jealous of the person who has what you want. We might observe that many people have things that we don't, but focusing on what others have leads us to become jealous. To combat this type of thinking, I have provided some suggestions for activities to train your mind to focus on the present moment, here and now.

Mindful activities can be as simple as mindful eating (eating with no distractions and being present with every bite) or mindful meditation (creating space to meditate for 10 to15 minutes by sitting in silence or listening to a guided meditation). I enjoy archery, which is a fantastic reminder to focus and be present each time I shoot an arrow from my recurve bow. It could also be practicing yoga or surfing, which requires you to focus on the activity so your mind is not distracted but present in the here and now. Find things that ground you and bring you back to reality. Be the best version of yourself by doing activities that bring you harmony.

GOAL PLANNING/ ACCOUNTABILITY

The act of goal planning is vital for making the most of your time and resources. It gives individuals motivation by helping them focus on short-term and long-term visions for their life. It also requires accountability from family, friends, or acquaintances to ensure you stay on track to attain your goals. I suggest that your partner not be the one to help you with accountability because this can complicate the relationship and potentially lead to resentment on both sides. Accountability can look different for each person. It could be sharing your goal(s) with someone else, asking them to check in with you every two weeks via a phone call, or perhaps downloading an accountability app or grabbing coffee with a friend on a Sunday afternoon. Some of the apps I recommend for this are HabitShare, getslash.co, or stickK. Ultimately, the purpose of this is to support you in accomplishing your goals. Make the process fun and creative so that you will look forward to it. I have focused on goal planning more intentionally in the past two years. I first listed small goals that I hoped to accomplish within three months that covered health, spirituality, career, and relationships. The process enabled me to make progress toward larger goals by requiring smaller, more attainable actions first; for example, I put this into practice by starting the dialogue with my manager about transitioning out of my jewelry position. This conversation was a smaller goal that eventually led to my now larger goal of launching this book and Antidote. This example is one of many as to how I have utilized the goal planning methods I share below.

There are numerous methods for setting goals. SMART Goals is currently a popular one; however, I will describe three other methods that I use.

The first method is called WOOP, which stands for Wish, Outcome, Obstacle, and Plan, and was created by Dr. Gabriele Oettingen, Professor of Psychology at New York University. This method can be used to achieve goals and change habits. It is supportive of a wide range of goals, but it may be more useful for smaller ones. It requires five minutes of undivided attention and can be done anywhere, i.e., during a lunch break at work.

Step 1 (1 min): What is it that you wish for? BE SPECIFIC.

Step 2 (1 min): What is the ideal outcome of this goal? What are you hoping to gain as a result?

Step 3 (1 to 2 min): What are the obstacles getting in the way of this goal? What is stopping you from getting the outcome you are seeking?

Step 4 (1 min): What actions will you take to get the outcome you want? What plan do you have in place to accomplish this goal?

Here is a personal example:

I want to read one book in April. The book will be *Sapiens* by Yuval Noah Harari. The outcome is that I finish this book and better understand human evolution and our history. I can share and discuss what I have learned during a book club meeting with my best friend, who will also be reading the book. The potential obstacles for me would be prioritizing TV or going out over reading every night. I get too tired some days and forgo my reading, leaving myself daunted by the task of catching up over the weekend. I plan to read for 30 minutes every night for one month and share this with my friend to hold me accountable. I will also set myself a reminder to read every night so that I do not forget.

The example I just shared is how I have successfully used the WOOP technique. I completed the book in one month and can now discuss the book's concepts with others. The method is simple and easy to use, so take your time and follow the steps listed above. For more information, see woopmylife.org or the WOOP mobile app.

The second method is a list of questions that support you with setting goals. These goals can be set and reviewed quarterly or annually. Create a template that will work best for you. They can be physically written down, placed in a Google Doc, or displayed as pictures. Choose a form that resonates with you. I suggest revisiting the document every few weeks to keep the information relevant and at the forefront of your mind.

Here are some questions to help you set your goals:

- List your number one most successful habit.
- What is the one thing you are most proud of?
- What are your core values?

- Where have you compromised your core values this quarter (or year)?
- What are you letting go of?
- What skills would you like to learn?
- Is there anything new you want to try?
- What are the three things you would like to add to your life this quarter (or year)?
- What are three things you would like to remove from your life this quarter (or year)?
- What would increase your quality of life? (i.e., prepaid massages, events, tennis, etc.)
- What is something you can do to celebrate?
- What are the worst things that can happen this quarter (or year)?
- How will you feel when you accomplish your goals this quarter (or year)?

This activity is accompanied by the Wheel of Life, which helps you visualize your life by looking at a visual representation of all areas at once. The wheel supports you with a better understanding of which parts of your life are flourishing and which require more work. The ultimate goal is to strive for a well-lived, meaningful life without neglecting any aspects of your life. You can find a template and a completed Wheel of Life sheet for reference under the Resources tab at: http://antidotehealth.io/?page_id=186.

Here are the instructions for completing the Wheel of Life: Rate the following areas from 1–10 (10 being the best):

- Fun and Recreation
- Career
- Money

- Health
- Relationships/Romance
- Personal Growth
- Friends and Family
- Physical Environment

Next, answer these questions:

- What are three things that would improve each area of the Wheel of Life?
- What is working? What is not working?
- What are three areas of the wheel that you want to bring up to a 10?

Follow-up for tracking previous quarterly or annual goals:

- How do you rate the quarter/year (from 1–10)?
- How would you summarize it in one sentence?
- What were the 20% of the people, things, and activities that made up 80% of your happiness?
- What were the 20% of the people, things, and activities that made up 80% of your sadness/stress?

Once you have answered these questions, you have completed your first goal-setting session. Give yourself some credit for a job well done, and now use these tools to support you in attaining your goals. Good luck!

The third method that I will share is creating your action plan. This method is to turn what you see for yourself into actions that will help you achieve your goals. The action plan has three parts: the heart, head, and hands. I learned about this specific breakdown in a course called The Science of

Success taught by Dr. Caproni.[1] She describes the first part, the heart, as identifying what is most important to you in life. In the second part, the head, you identify one area you will work on in the short term to move you toward achieving your goals. The third part, the hands, involves creating the steps you will take in the short term to make progress in that specific area. This technique supports you in appreciating and celebrating small wins and learning to face setbacks with resilience and self-love. I found Dr. Caproni's action plan very useful in completing this book. I will provide the goal of writing this book as an example.

First, address the heart, head, and hands of your goal.

Heart: What are your values, and what is most meaningful to you in life?

Head: What is the time required to accomplish the goal? Consider priorities, feasibility, trade-offs, and what others need from you.

Hands: What specific actions will you take to implement your plan?

Second, create a diagram or list that identifies three or more parts of your life that are most important to you, i.e., family, community, and career. Then explain why each is important to you.

Third, for each item on your list, write down three or more goals you want to achieve within that category; for example, in the career category, you could list the goal of achieving a promotion.

Fourth, of all the goals listed in the previous step, choose only one goal that you want to focus on right now—for example, publishing a book. Then come up with a few obstacles that could potentially inhibit you from attaining that goal, i.e., not taking the initiative to write consistently for a few hours a day or spending time watching TV instead of writing. Next, identify at least one thing you will stop doing or modify so you can devote more time and effort to achieving your goal; for example, I limited TV time to only one hour a day to focus on writing.

Fifth, create an action plan using your own template or the one I have provided at http://antidotehealth.io/?page_id=186 to document three or more specific steps to achieve the goal you identified. When creating the plan, include the following information: What is my goal? What is my deadline for completing my goal? Who will I tell about my plan (accountability/support)? How will I measure my success?

On the next page is my completed action plan for writing my book:

What is the goal: Publish Memoir

Be very specific, what will I do		Start Date	Completion Date	Who will I share this information with?	How will I measure my progress?
First Action:	I will write my memoir and enjoy every minute of it.	April 5	July 30	Therapist, Shiv, Manpreet	Create a reminder and schedule that allocates 3 - 4 hours of writing/ free thought every other day.
Second Action:	Proofread/Feedback; Edit then distribute to peers	August 5	September 30	Therapist, Shiv, Manpreet	Create a list of peers to share a copy of my book and find a service to support with proofreading. Make a proofreading schedule.
Third Action:	Self-publish book on Amazon Kindle Direct, BookRix, Apple E-book store, etc.	November 11	Jan 2021	Therapist, Shiv, Manpreet	Confirm list of publishing platforms. Bind a hard copy of the book as a celebration of completion.

Once you have followed these steps and created an action plan for one or more specific goal(s), then you have completed your goal-setting session. The purpose of goal setting is to strive for a meaningful life, which is not necessarily a balanced life because balance can shift at any moment. Instead of focusing on balance, which is ever-changing, focus on meaning, and appreciation for your current life. Plans and circumstances can change, so be easy on yourself when this happens. All you need to do is go back to your document and revise it. The goal is to strive for a well-lived, meaningful life that you are grateful to be living.

I have personally used all three of these methods at different points in my life and for other goals that I am working toward. There are plenty of options for creating your goal-setting plan or technique, so please find what works for you. I wish you the best of luck and hope that this supports you.

MEDITATION, BREATHING EXERCISES, AND BODY SCANNING

Meditation is the mental exercise of training your mind to free itself of anxieties by focusing on mental relaxation and the present moment. The goal is to gain awareness and mindfulness by removing reactivity to negative thoughts in order to have healthy thoughts and emotions.

Meditation has many benefits for your well-being, including relaxation and the reduction of stress, anxiety, and depression. In addition, meditation promotes better sleep, reduces inflammation, and creates a more positive outlook on life. Honestly, the list goes on. I began practicing meditation when I made the decision to move to San Diego. My anxiety was consuming me because of the uncertainty of leaving a secure job and my family home in pursuit of following my dreams. Practicing healthy habits calmed my nerves, giving me the clarity to set intentions and take action. I now had the tools to shift out of analysis paralysis. Since that time, I have practiced meditation first thing every morning to ease any stress from the previous day and gain a new perspective for my day ahead.

I encourage you to begin by meditating for ten minutes every day to support you in building the skill and gaining consistency. It is natural to notice your mind wandering—we are human! Do not judge yourself for this; it is about practice, not perfection. There are many different ways to incorporate meditation into your daily life to improve your well-being.

Meditation can either be done in silence or guided by a teacher. There are many resources I find helpful on the Insight Timer app or YouTube. These are free resources I have used to get general or specific meditations. If you are not interested in guided meditation, then try silent meditation. It may not be easy at first, but I would recommend this practice once you have built your confidence in meditating. You will notice more "noise" in your mind than in a guided meditation, so there will be times of judgment and questioning whether this form of meditation works or not. This is an expected part of the process, especially for beginners, so do not get discouraged. Instead, allow yourself to experience the noise, and over time it will quiet down.

Begin by finding a quiet space to sit or lie down. I would suggest focusing on your breath and any bodily sensations, or a word, affirmation, or mantra to decrease distraction and provide focus. An example would be the word "peace" or the affirmation "My confidence knows no limits."

To support you with tracking your meditations, place a daily reminder on your phone to meditate for at least ten minutes. Insight Timer also has an excellent tracking method incorporated for both timed and guided meditations. The information is logged automatically, which helps encourage you to continue the practice. Other resources may better suit your interests or needs, but consider my suggestions if you need a starting point. In addition to meditation, breathing exercises have similar effects on your well-being to support your overall health.

Breathing exercises help your mind relax and focus on the present while relieving stress and anxiety and improving sleep. There are many forms of breathing exercises, but here are a few that you can try. Choose what is most comfortable for you.

Begin by either lying down or moving to a seated position. Find a quiet space to support your focus and allocate at least ten minutes to gain the benefits of this exercise.

Practice one of these methods:

Sama Vritti: Breathe through your nose: four counts in, four counts out. Repeat the process for at least ten minutes.

Abdominal Breathing: Place one hand on your chest and the other on your belly. Take a deep breath in through your nose, inflating the diaphragm with air and stretching your lungs, then exhale slowly. During this process, try to contract your hands and feet to release any tension in your body. Repeat the process for at least ten minutes.

Alternating Nostril Breathing: Using your thumb and index finger, begin pressing your thumb against one nostril (closing airflow) to inhale deeply through the other (open) nostril. Once you inhale, release the thumb, press your index finger on the outside of your other nostril, and exhale. Once you have done this for a few minutes, switch sides and inhale through the other nostril. The same rules apply. Repeat the process for at least ten minutes.

4-7-8 Breathing: Exhale air through your mouth, then inhale air through your nose for four counts. Then, hold your breath for seven counts, and release all of the air for eight counts. Repeat the process for at least ten minutes.

Pursed Lip Breathing: Take in a breath for two counts, then pucker your lips to exhale for four counts. Repeat the process for at least ten minutes.

All breathing exercises require repetition, so be easy on yourself and allow yourself to relax.

Lastly, as a part of meditation, body scanning can be useful in gaining overall wellness through mindful scanning of your body for pain, tension, and any unwanted feelings. The goal is to connect to your physical body so your mind and body are in sync. Once you gain consistency with this practice, you will notice an improvement in sleep, anxiety, stress, and compassion.

Step 1: Lie down and close your eyes.

Step 2: Begin focusing on your breath, then choose a part of your body you want to focus on while breathing deeply. Notice if you are feeling sensations of pain, tension, or anything else.

Step 3: Spend about thirty seconds to one minute. If you notice any unwanted feelings, acknowledge them without judgment, then imagine decreasing the unwanted feelings by breaking away from them.

Step 4: Move to another part of your body and practice steps 2–4 until you have fully scanned your entire body.

All of the practices mentioned above can be done anywhere. All you need is ten minutes of your time and a quiet space to focus your energy. Stay encouraged by including others in these activities or logging your time to watch your progress. The key is to enjoy the journey and allow yourself to let go. Enjoy!

ABOUT THE AUTHOR

Hiral Patel is inspired by the resilience of people daring to thrive with kidney disease. She embodies the spirit of a social entrepreneur. She is passionate about supporting others to break the stigma of kidney disease by equipping them with the tools required to be empowered and effectively advocate for themselves. Her vision is to raise the spirits and awareness of people facing adversity by offering the beauty of community support through her online platform, Antidote. The purpose of Antidote is to bridge the gap of support and resources so others can build connections throughout their journey.

Hiral holds a bachelor's degree in anthropology with a minor in finance from California State University, Northridge. After receiving her kidney transplant, her focus shifted to advocacy for patients—first with a local support group and now through her platform Antidote. Born and raised in Los Angeles, Hiral now enjoys sunny San Diego, CA, with her fiancé, Shiv. The essence of her being is built on filling her soul with the discovery of new adventures and embracing life. She cherishes moments spent connecting with her family and friends, and with nature.

CAN YOU HELP ME?

Thank You for Reading My Book!

I truly appreciate all of your feedback, and I love hearing what you have to say.

I value your input to make the next version of this book and my future books better.

Please leave me an honest review on Amazon letting me know your thoughts about the book.

Thanks so much!

Love & Light
Hiral Patel

ANTIDOTE: WHAT YOU NEED TO KNOW

Antidote is an easy-to-use platform that creates an interactive experience for users to engage with others in a forum. In addition to the main forum available to kidney patients, there are subforums specifically for the different activities I have shared with you in this book. The forums, along with additional resources, including articles and lifestyle tips conducive to your well-being, provide a holistic approach to serving your needs. The goal is to create a supportive, engaging, and immersive platform that encourages you to thrive on your journey with kidney disease. It also provides a haven for caregivers and other people living with a debilitating chronic illness to share their experiences with each activity. I envision this platform expanding outside the context of a website to include a user-friendly, interactive, and accessible mobile application. The goal is to create an inclusive community that shares the belief that challenges are more manageable when faced together. So, I ask you to please join me on this adventure of making Antidote all that we seek in a supportive community by sharing your story and supporting others in sharing theirs. Now is your moment to share at http://antidotehealth.io—your ally in health!

NOTES

Social Capital

1. Dr. Paula Caproni, *The Science of Success:* University of Michigan Course.

Setting Healthy Boundaries

1. Joaquín Selva, "How to Set Healthy Boundaries: 10 Examples + PDF Worksheets," *Positive Psychology*, 14 April 2020, https://positivepsychology.com/great-self-care-setting-healthy-boundaries/.
2. Dr. Henry Cloud and Dr. John Townsend, *Boundaries, Updated and Expanded Edition: When to Say Yes, How to Say No to Take Control of Your Life* (Grand Rapids: Zondervan, 1992), 161.

Mindfulness

1. Giridhari Das. Course Bhagavad Gita. Course Bhagavad Gita. https://3tpath.com/teachings/.

Goal Planning/ Accountability

1. Dr. Paula Caproni, *The Science of Success:* University of Michigan Course.

Made in the USA
Coppell, TX
12 February 2021